Driving Finish

Also by Carol Madeline Smith and published
by Robson Books
Driving Force

Driving Finish

Carol Madeline Smith

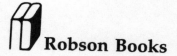

Robson Books

First published in Great Britain in 1994
by Robson Books Ltd, Bolsover House,
5–6 Clipstone Street, London W1P 7EB

**British Library Cataloguing in
Publication Data**
A catalogue record for this title is
available from the British Library

ISBN 0 86051 713 6

Printed and bound in Great Britain by WBC,
Bridgend, Mid Glam.

This book is dedicated to the memory of my friend Cyril Coke, who sustained my faith in it and gave it a title, but who tragically did not live to see its completion.

1

Hope

A thin, sharp wind prowled up the alley and crept through the gaps in the ill-fitting door to attack my feet and legs even behind the desk where I sat. The chill, amplified by the dreary damp of the shop, spread upwards and inwards until it seemed to seep into my bones and my very spirit. No thermal underwear could repel the hypothermic depression of 'Ted's Shed' and I had to keep busy, keep moving and keep making endless cups of scalding tea. When there were customers to see to, or even furniture to arrange or clean, that was easier to achieve; but by early afternoon on a Saturday trade just seemed to melt away. I often argued that it was pointless staying open but a customer might call in, or there just might be a last-minute phone call. There might be an urgent house clearance to do and we could oblige, at a little extra cost, on a Sunday and thus make an extra bob or two. God knew, we needed every penny we could find.

On that raw Saturday afternoon in early November however, I just sat there. My morbid thoughts multiplied as the cold and damp paralysed me. The feeble sputterings of the little gas heater beside the desk stood no chance of making any climatic impression on that dismal mausoleum of a warehouse.

For about the hundredth time that afternoon I asked

myself how on earth I had come to this, making a living out of the detritus of other people's homes and lives. I was trying to sell items I would personally have donated to the local bonfire rather than put in my home, goods which had been sold to us in the first place because no one in the family wanted them – or else someone in the family needed the money more. They would be bought by a single parent or someone on the dole with a Giro from the DHSS: three-piece suite, £59; single bed, £49; electric cooker, £69; table and chairs £45. And all from a dark, decaying warehouse situated half-way up a dark, decaying alley. Old Ted, who had first set away his empire of sordid grot in the premises, was long since gone to the great furniture emporium in the sky, but the name still stuck. Indelibly. And I was beginning to feel that my life was stuck in that place. Indelibly. And I loathed and hated it. I willed the hands of the clock to crawl further towards the blessed release of five o'clock so that I could get home to a bath and warmth and sanity once more. So – how on earth?

Well, the unlikely answer presented itself as always; because of a horse, and because of a man. And now because of another horse.

It had not always been thus for me. I had spent my early childhood in colonial opulence in Nigeria and the rest at a very good private school. I had been a teacher once; a career woman with a Head of Departmentship in my grasp. And then I'd been a lady of leisure, a member of the County set, running my life from a five-bedroomed farm house and hunting to hounds on a Wednesday. Two marriages and many painful memories lay behind me. When recurring gynaecological problems finally resulted in two drastic operations by the age of thirty-one, I somehow weathered the physical impact but not the mental and the resultant emotional chaos rocked my life to its core. When the dust finally settled it was upon a second marriage that was an empty shell. With a determination born out of the belief that life had to hold *something*, I turned my back upon financial security and social standing and set off to go it alone. Many acquaintances considered, perhaps rightly, that this was the final and ultimate manifestation of my mental imbalance.

However, when I say 'go it alone' I do not mean it literally, for with me went my two most precious companions: my daughter Megan and my Welsh Cob, Conwy Blaze, better known as Bear. Megan was three years old at the time and Bear around ten, which meant that he and I had been together for seven years. The shaggy little native creature that I had bought as a three-year-old with a £300 legacy left to me by my eccentric Great-aunt Meg had blossomed and been transformed into a superb, fit hunting horse with whom I had shared many splendid days' sport before we both got bitten by the driving bug. Within months of his being broken to harness he was competing at national level in three-day driving events, and he came third in the single-horse class at the National Championships in 1980. He had a brilliant future ahead of him, I was told.

Then disaster struck. He walked over a septic tank covered by rotten timbers which collapsed, and he was trapped up to his nostrils in stinking slurry. It took three vets, two fire engines, a dozen men and a JCB to get him out. He lost a third of the skin and hair on his back with septic friction burns. He had emphysema and had strained his heart.

It was a miracle he had no broken bones, the vet said. A miracle he was alive at all. I should content myself with that fact and accept that he would never compete again. But I could not accept it; refused to accept it. And time, the best medical treatment, a lot of love – and possibly another miracle – brought him back to peak fitness. That he should have his chance again, that he should show just how talented and special he was, became the literal driving force behind my life.

It was impractical, it was unreasonable, to walk out of total security with a horse and a small girl and expect that I could afford either the time or the money to compete at driving events at any level, let alone at the very top. But total dedication to a cause – particularly when it's the only one you've got – can sometimes result in a form of tunnel vision. And the last thing I had expected to find in the middle of my tunnel was Richard Smith.

The initial impression I had of him never appreciably altered: short, fat, bald, middle-aged and fifteen years older than me. He had been a coal miner, then a soldier, then an antiques dealer. He was every bit as obsessed with carriage driving as I was – and much better at it. The other thing we had in common was that we were both at crossroads in our lives and marriages, and not at all sure where we wanted to go. So we tentatively set along the road together with the only goal for him to drive Bear back into form that season.

We had gone but a few steps along that road before disaster struck again. I was riding a friend's young and green Dales mare and not totally concentrating on the job in hand when she reared, fell on me and made a pretty fair demolition job of my pelvis and right hip. I returned to my cottage, my daughter and my horse two months and two operations later, on crutches and with a wheelchair. I also returned to a man I hardly knew – but one who had stood by me through all the dark weeks.

So we threw our lots in together on a more permanent basis and headed along a road which, if it had been ill defined before, was now positively treacherous. I had a small amount of capital from my divorce settlement. We could have had a nicely modernized modest terrace house with central heating, double glazing and low rates. Instead we bought a totally diabolical, uninhabitable carcass of a house with a range of decrepit outbuildings and ten acres of badly fenced, badly drained, weed-infested land called Mount Pleasant Farm. Well, we had to get our priorities right, didn't we? We had to have somewhere to keep Bear. And just to prove that we were totally committed to our dream, or unhinged, or both, I splashed out to buy the thing we needed the most in the world to make our dream come true: another young Welsh Cob, whom we called Blizzard. For single-horse competition was no challenge to Richard Smith: he was a pairs driver.

Throughout this period we did in fact manage to achieve a perfectly secure and suitable home environment for ourselves and Megan. Admittedly for a while it was from a static caravan, and then from a small rented terraced house, but we were always clean and warm and happy and busy, so what need anything bigger or more opulent? Finally, with the sweat of our brows and the toil of our hands we rebuilt, redecorated and moved into our own house and settled down to making our living and then spending the major proportion of it on our dream: being selected for the British team for the first-ever World Championship for Pairs of Horses to be held at Sandringham in 1985. This living had to be made from Ted's Shed, the gruesome warehouse in Bishop Auckland.

Our selection for the British team for the first World Championships gave us an elation it is impossible to describe. All the disasters, all the heartache and hardship became suddenly and totally worthwhile. We threw ourselves into a frenzy of preparation and travelled the country for weeks on end with the horses, competing and training them to a peak of fitness. The business was left to God and casual hired help.

When Richard stood on the podium with the rest of the British team to receive their bronze medals from Prince Philip I felt I should burst with pride and joy. The glory of that moment would, I was sure, sustain me throughout whatever trials and tribulations life could throw in my face. But we were to find that glory alone does not pay rent, or rates, or food, or clothes; or provide hay, straw, oats and shoes for two healthy horses. We had achieved our goal, but in doing so we had nearly let our livelihood slip from our grasp.

We pared our budget to the core. The horses were simply turned out to grass, the groom we had employed for the summer went home to Wales. Shop staff were cut and I had to plug the gap. But as the pile of bills and ugly letters grew ever higher, I began to fear that it might all be too late. By working hard and keeping to the strict bare necessities of life we should have been able to manage and keep our home and business running. But bare necessities did not include Bear's necessities, nor Blizzard's necessities, come to that: competing our pair of carriage driving horses was quite simply an extravagance we could no longer afford. And that was why, I smiled grimly to myself, because of a horse and because of a man and because of yet another horse, I was fighting a losing battle against hypothermia and depression on a grey November Saturday afternoon in Ted's Shed.

The irony was that, although the horses had led us down the rocky path to near ruination, they could also be our salvation from it. For if we sold everything, the horses, the harness, the carriages, the horsebox and then of course Mount Pleasant Farm, the problems would all be solved. We could go and buy our two-up, two-down modernized terraced house with central heating and double glazing and live happily ever after.

'Live happily?' my spirit jeered at me. 'With no hoof-beats clattering into the yard, no eager whinnies from the stables telling you it's tea-time?' My relationship with Richard had been founded on and in the main sustained by our joint obsession with the horses. Without them, if I was brutally honest with myself, I realized that we had very little in common.

However, the unpalatable truth was that something had to be done, and it had to be fairly drastic. Selling Blizzard seemed to be the first and logical step. He was young and superb, had won a World bronze medal and had a long career ahead of him.

But to sell Bear? We had shared ten long years of disasters and triumphs together and bolstered each other through them all. No. Whatever happened, Bear would remain mine, though not perhaps remain *with* me. If I had nowhere to keep a horse would I have enough money to rent grazing? I doubted if I could afford to keep him in livery somewhere. He was thirteen years old: how could I reduce him to roaming around on scrub grazing, out all winter, when he had grown used to the four-star hotel treatment of clean, warm blankets, soft, deep beds and three good meals a day? Perhaps it would be kinder to let him go on loan to a good driving home to do the job he loved and was best at for a few more years. Perhaps things would improve, perhaps he could come back some day. But to dwell on the thought of Bear leaving me forever left a sickening ache in the very centre of my being. Our lives were too intertwined, our debts to each other too deep.

I was brought sharply back from my miserable reflections to miserable reality by the telephone ringing. I was reluctant to pick up the phone. I expected to hear, 'Me Nana's died, and there's some stuff we want shot of. Will yer come and hev a look arrit?' The family vultures would have picked the carcass of the house clean and Richard would go and find the sad and unpalatable bones: the black vinyl suite, the twenty-year-old cooker, a broken formica table and a smelly, threadbare carpet. Would life ever hold anything for me again except being stuck in that wretched shop trying to buy and sell endlessly gruesome household goods?

The phone was still ringing insistently. 'Good afternoon. Can I help you?' I asked, in the deliberately cultured and pleasant voice I used out of pure perversity.

'Is that Ted's Shed?' a man's voice enquired. 'Richard Smith's shop? Richard Smith who drives the horses?'

'Yes,' I replied cautiously.

'So I've found you at last!' he exclaimed.

My heart skipped three beats and then went into fast-freeze. What if he was a debt collector, a bailiff? I hadn't known such personages existed before meeting Richard Smith, but I had been trying to keep one step ahead of them ever since I had.

'Listen, I hope you don't mind me phoning. Actually it's taken me weeks and weeks to track you down. I saw the interview you did a couple of months ago on television about the World Championships.'

A stupid lump was forming in my throat. Only a couple of months ago! The World Championships and our brief moment of fame when the horses had graced the region's evening television screens. We had talked of our struggle to get to the top, the financial problems of staying there and our fears for the future.

'Hello? They were your horses, weren't they? I have got the right people?'

'Yes,' I said quietly. 'That was us.'

'I happened to be at my brother-in-law's house the evening the programme was on and he was really taken with it, really taken. He's been going to Lowther Driving Trials every summer for five years now to watch the horses and carriages. Takes the whole family and stays there for the week. Thinks it's wonderful. He's the chairman of a large international company in Darlington that does shopfittings for supermarkets and so on. When I said that I thought I recognized your husband from when I was in the Bishop and Crook area, and remembered him driving a pair of horses around the streets, he said that if I could track

your husband down and give him his phone number there
might be a mutually beneficial arrangement that could be
made. So, would you like his phone number?'

I wrote it down with a trembling hand in huge numerals,
quite obliterating the 'today's calls' page in the book on
the desk.

'I'm not making you any promises,' he was saying. 'But
he must still be interested because when I saw him last
week he asked me if I'd tracked you down yet. So, anyway,
it's worth a try. Give him a ring and the best of luck!'

'Who exactly is "he"?' I screeched hysterically, fearing
he was about to put the phone down. 'I mean, who do I
ring?'

'Ask for Mr Robson. Alan Robson.'

I was oblivious to the cold and damp, my blood surged
and tingled through my body till my cheeks flushed. I
switched off the gas, locked the desk and, grabbing my
coat, headed for the door. Just as I was putting the lights
off the phone rang again. I was back to it in two strides.

'Hello!' I said excitedly.

'Hello? Ted's Shed? Listen, Aa've gorra suite Aa want
rid of, can you tek it tomorra?'

'Sorry,' I lilted brightly, 'we're closed for the weekend.
Phone on Monday!'

I didn't even bother to take his name and address. I
slammed the door behind me and headed for my battered
13 year old Mini. But I didn't feel weary any more, I was
oblivious of the grey, raw day. I even played football with
the discarded fish and chip papers that were blowing
down the alley. For the only truly deficient thing in my life
had just been replenished.

Hope.

2

Aye-Aye

'Chairman of an International Shopfitting Company' was how Alan Robson had been described to us. On the phone he sounded absolutely charming – would it be all right for him to bring his wife? We tidied everything and everywhere to the very best of our ability but somehow all I saw was shabbiness. And our home-made cross-country carriage standing to attention on the cracked concrete in case a drive out was called for looked – well – home-made.

It was all very well eulogizing about British teams and World Bronze Medals on the phone, listing event locations such as Royal Windsor, Sandringham and Floors Castle.

This was reality. This was Stanley Crook, County Durham. Category D Pit Village and winner of the 'last place God created and somehow forgot to finish' award.

My imagination saw the wife of the Chairman of a large international company as tall, elegant, cool, poised, picking her way on Italian heels around the embarrassing little heaps the horses were bound to produce as soon as they came out of the stable, aquiline nostrils quivering as the breeze brought a faint but clinging aroma of eau de muck-heap into the yard. Nibbling a scone out of courtesy with one hand while leafing through her calorie-counter with the other. Unable to disguise her relief when it was time

10

to go. 'Well, it's been *so* nice meeting you . . .' and on the way home in the car, 'You're not *serious* about this, darling?'

A big, black BMW cruised very slowly down Stanley front street. Fumbling to rip my pinny off and waving like an idiot, I pointed the way to turn in and come up our tooth-rattling back street. I prayed that BMWs had decent suspension. With an engine note that sounded like a contented purr, the shiny black car slid to halt in the lee of Richard's battered transit van. And out got Alan Robson – and his wife..

'Hello, I'm Chris!' said a petite short-haired lady dressed in camel sweater, trousers and sensible flat shoes. She handed me a large carrier bag.

'Apples for your horses – we've had so many windfalls this year. I'm sick of making pies!'

I took the bag from her gratefully. 'Would you like to come in the house and have a cup of tea and a scone?'

'Oh, I could just murder a cuppa,' she grinned.

As we headed indoors I realized we had lost both Richard and Alan, but as they were last seen headed towards the stables I didn't worry.

When, some two hours later, the shiny black car slid away as effortlessly as it had arrived, I was left dizzy with the speed – and the simplicity – of the afternoon's events. What Alan Robson wanted for his company was an opportunity to invite guests, prospective as well as well-established clients, to partake of corporate hospitality that was different to the usual sporting fixtures Chairmen take their clients to.

Alan had been to Horse Driving Trials at the Lowther event in Cumbria for the previous five summers and admitted a secret desire to get up and have a go at this driving lark himself. And so the horses were brought out, harnessed up and away they went; Richard and Alan, Bear and Blizzard with all of our combined hopes and fears for the future rolling along with the wheels of Richard's home-made carriage. And by the time they returned, the direction of our futures – all our futures – had changed in a way I couldn't have dreamt possible.

Within two weeks contracts were signed and the first quarter's sponsorship cheque was safely in the bank. Colours for logos and jumpers were chosen and beautiful, soft pure wool show rugs were ordered for the cobs. Pearl grey and edged in black and red, one side bore their name and the other side proclaimed 'Montan Group' above which, proudest of all, was displayed the Union Jack – the flag that Bear and Blizzard were entitled to wear with honour since their selection to represent their country the previous year. Even Plod, dear old faithful Plod, Richard's venerable horsebox, was to receive a transforming face-lift – red and grey paintwork with a gigantic Montan 'M' logo on each side.

To me, it was the generosity of heart behind the deal that mattered as much as the financial support.

Nevertheless, when Richard and I sat down to our first 'campaign' meeting for the next year there were certain priorities to be got in order. It quickly became apparent we just could not do without a new head groom.

We had had to let our hot-blooded, red-headed, totally devoted Welsh groom, Chris Morris-Jones, go a few months previously when funds ran out. We were without staff, which whilst the cobs were let down and at grass was fine, I could cope on my own even though I was working at the shop most days. But once they came back into regular work, it would be a different matter. They needed a regular routine, carefully monitored care and frequent feeding, and neither Richard or I would be there to do it. And what was more, one groom would not be sufficient, we really needed two. The horses needed to be ridden out as a pair as well as worked individually. At shows one groom was certainly not enough with all the humping and carrying and heavy work to do. If the groom we employed was the holder of the British Horse Society Assistant Instructor Certificate – in other words, trained to teach riding – then we would be eligible to take on a YTS trainee, as we would have a qualified instructor. So I was given the task of composing an advert for *Horse and Hound*, stating that Richard Smith, British Team World Bronze Medalist for pairs driving (well, if you've got it, flaunt it!) required an AI to supervise his horses and partake in the forthcoming carriage-driving season. Live in as family; all meals provided. I prayed nightly that my little advert in *Horse and Hound* would reap a rich harvest of talented, experienced riders all queueing to come and train our horses.

In the event I had two replies.

The first was from a young lady down South somewhere, who as soon as she discovered she was not to have her own private bathroom but would have to share ours, lost interest.

The second, to my great surprise and intense curiosity, came from a young man. He lived in Rothbury in Northumberland – the next county up to Durham. The young man's name was Alastair Parkin.

Did I have time to pop across to the little shop opposite us I wondered? I had made scones for the forthcoming interview and had run myself rather low on milk for the tea. I had a quarter of an hour – that should be plenty of time. Richard always said, rather rudely I thought, that surviving my 'brown bricks' was the acid test for any newcomer. I grabbed the nearest anorak, the tatty one I did the stables in, decided just to leave my slippers on and slipped out quickly. Clutching my bottle of milk I waited on the opposite side of the road for a brand new four-wheel-drive Panda to pass the house. But it didn't pass. It pulled up at the kerb, a window rolled down and a clean-

shaven, strikingly good-looking young man in an obviously very expensive designer-knit sweater smiled broadly
and said hopefully, 'Excuse me, I'm looking for Mount
Pleasant Farm?'

I felt, in my slippers and tatty anorak, clutching my milk
bottle, that I only needed a hair net to make a passable
impression of Ena Sharples. As I crossed the road, feeling
rather foolish, I focused more closely on the beautiful
sweater. It was beige with a motif of galloping horses all
the way round.

'You must be Alastair,' I ventured.

'Yes! And you? Are you Carol by any chance? What a
stroke of luck!'

He was as well spoken as he was dressed, which made
me shuffle all the more uncomfortably in my slippers, but
I smiled back graciously and gave him directions to get
him up our bumpy back street – which gave me time to
fly into the house and grab my shoes.

Over the tea and scones I kept wondering again and
again just who was interviewing whom. The list of this
young man's previous equestrian experiences was impressive to say the least. Trained by a top eventer in Scotland
and then over to France to work at a showjumping yard.
Now recently returned from New Zealand from running
an event yard there. I knew we had a World Bronze Medal
to our name but – gosh! – I was impressed.

'You realize that we require someone not only to school
the horses and run the yard but to train a student on the
YTS Scheme? That's why we need an AI.'

'Well, I'm a BHSII, actually.'

'Aye – Aye?' I repeated doubtfully. 'Does that mean you
can't teach?'

His smile, looking back on it now, was very gracious –
all things considered.

'Actually, an "II" is a considerably higher British Horse

Society qualification than an "AI". I'm sure I would be able to teach your trainee satisfactorily.'

It was perhaps my merciful ignorance that kept me from realizing just what a fool I had been. That did not hit me for quite a long while: until I found out that for every thirty or so 'AIs' there is probably only one 'II'. That the initials stood for something neither nautical nor slightly naughty but for 'Intermediate Instructor'. That there was only one qualification higher, that of 'I' or 'Instructor'. But most of all, that at twenty-two, and now well on his way towards his 'I' qualification, young Mr Parkin must be an exceptionally accomplished horseman and teacher. As it was, in my blissful ignorance, I simply looked relieved and said 'Oh well that's all right then. Another scone?'

'Oh, yes please – they are delicious; have you made them yourself?'

Richard's look was of plain astonishment; mine of delighted smugness. Though had I been more astute I should have realized then that anyone whose appetite could accommodate four of my 'brown bricks' was going to make a significant impact on the grocery bill.

A tour of the yard and horses followed tea. Our by now shaggy 15.1 cobs looked decidedly dwarfed by Alastair's six foot two frame and he, with all his tact and charm, could not hide his disappointment when he saw them. They certainly looked far more impressive on the photos in the house, gleaming in their copper summer coats, powering through water hazards in clouds of spray. Standing there on hairy legs, peacefully chewing away on hay nets even I had to admit that they did not look like world beaters.

Back in the house I felt I really couldn't believe my ears when Alastair said yes, he would like to do the season with us; yes, he would accept the very modest wage we had to offer. Curiosity overcame me at this point.

'Excuse me for asking you this, but why?'

'Why?' Alastair looked puzzled.

'Yes, why would someone as well qualified and well experienced as yourself with a global passport work-wise want to come to Stanley Crook and take on our modest establishment and horses? We must seem pretty small fry after what you've been used to.'

'Well I'll be honest. It's obviously not the money! But I set myself the goal of trying all aspects of the equestrian world before deciding what I truly wanted to do. I've tried most areas now – dressage, jumping, hunting, eventing. But one thing I know nothing whatsoever about is carriage driving and I'd like to give it a try.'

'When would you like to begin?' Richard enquired.

'Well we're nearly to Christmas now; shall we make a start of it in the New Year?'

'Good idea,' I agreed. 'That will give me a few weeks to find a suitable YTS trainee for you.'

By the time Alastair started I had indeed found a trainee, but she was probably the last person he would have considered as suitable. Sharon was sent to us for interview by the local equestrian training agency. She was small, had curly black hair and a fresh face. She was 'not long left school', and when the agency admitted to her having 'some learning difficulties' what they really meant was she could barely read or write. She was, they told me, a slow learner, and I soon discovered that this meant everything had to be repeated several times and then repeated back before we could be sure an instruction had been understood. Then she would carry it out to the letter – *exactly* to the letter – which meant we had to be very careful about *exactly* what we said. But she was likeable and hardworking, and she lived locally. This was another bonus, as our spare accommodation was taken by Alastair.

And so we emerged into the first week of 1986 full of hope, new plans and a totally new image. Within a few weeks the yard, the horses and even Richard and I wondered what had hit us. I had been doing everything alone and on a 'minimal necessity' basis since Chris Morris-Jones had left us, but even Chris in full Celtic swing had never shaken the yard up as radically as this.

Yard brooms lasted between two and three weeks before Alastair apologetically presented me with the bald wooden heads for renewal. After each feed every bucket, feed dish, spoon and corn measure would be washed, dried and hung, each to its own hook, in the feed room. Tack wouldn't have time to cool from being stripped off a horse's head or back before it was attacked with a damp sponge and saddle soap, buffed to a polish and hung symmetrically on newly labelled pegs in the harness room. The floor of the harness room was now hoovered every day, and even *we* didn't dare go in without taking our wellies off. The horses' winter coats ('Such a nuisance! Hold so much muck and grease! Prevent the horses cooling quickly!') were whisked off, and their tails, which we didn't bother much with over the winter months, were now cleanly washed, silky and untangled at all times.

We had a few sticky moments when the time came to begin riding the Boys. Alastair had announced a carefully drawn up programme of slow fittening work to get them ready for Richard to start driving.

'Actually,' I told him, 'I think you'll find they take very little getting fit. They've been stabled every night and kept on hay and some hard feed, and I've been riding a couple of times a week and Richard has had the odd drive.'

'Yes, but even so . . .' Alastair was obviously searching for tactful words. 'To be honest, they are actually just like large native ponies.'

I think Alastair was a little stunned by the vehemence of my reaction. 'Overgrown native ponies they may look like,' I managed to get out in a fairly dignified manner, 'but overgrown native ponies they do not *act* like. 15.1 may seem small to you, but when it is all muscle and heart, with a dash of Welsh fire in the belly, I think you'll find they are all the horse you would ever wish or want to handle.

'Look,' I went on, 'I apologize for that. I didn't mean it to sound the way it did. Why don't you just take them out for a ride and judge how unfit they are?'

I always rode Bear in a dog-legged military bit with a curb chain and two reins.

'Isn't that bit rather severe?' he asked. 'Since I'm just going to take him in the field and see how he is, I think I can manage to keep him under control in a snaffle. You should always preserve a snaffle mouth if it's possible, you know.'

'Oh, of course,' I agreed. It must have been more than six years since Bear had had a simple snaffle in his mouth, and weeks now since I'd exercised him on grass. Grass underfoot to Bear was like putting high-octane fuel into an already powerful car: he moved up about three gears and steering became rather more difficult. 'You'll find a nice piece of flat grass behind the reservoir wall.' I didn't add that it was a nice piece of flat grass where I always rewarded Bear with an exhilarating gallop after concentrated schooling.

He did not let me down.

Alastair's reins became shorter and shorter, Bear's neck became thicker and thicker and his nostrils wider and wider. Chin on chest and knees nearly to chin, he trotted round the perimeter of the field at a tooth – and other delicate parts – rattling pace. The more Alastair pulled, the more Bear pulled back. There was no question of Alastair being out of control or Bear unseating him, but Bear was enjoying himself in his own wicked way.

I waved solicitously from my position at the end of the wall and whether Bear took this as a signal or Alastair had decided enough was enough I don't know – but the next minute a blur of chestnut and white legs was pounding over the grass at full gallop and as they drew near, Alastair was hauling desperately on the reins to bring him to a halt, by sheer brute strength, a few feet from me.

'He's got no manners! No steering, no brakes and no mouth! He's stubborn and cantankerous . . .'

'He's all of those things and a lot more.' I replied. 'But I don't use that bit: you might as well try to ride him with an elastic band in his mouth.'

Alastair looked a little sheepish now.

'Well,' he admitted with a grin, 'for a horse that hasn't worked for four months, he's incredible. Even that gallop across there hasn't made him blow.'

'Why don't you take him back to the stable, change his bit and bring him out again for dressage? I think he's proved his point. Now it's time for you to prove yours.'

Bear didn't let me down this time either. At a beautifully cadenced and regular stride he trotted slowly, powerfully and elegantly in straight lines, diagonals and circles. He executed perfect shoulder-ins and crossed his legs beautifully to do a half-pass. Gradually they began to flow together. Gradually the magic began and what magic it was with such talented and sympathetic hands and legs blending with Bear's own body movements. The more Alastair relaxed and sat in the saddle, the more flexible and relaxed Bear became. It was like watching a ballet. Finally Alastair halted, reined back for three steps and stood four square and stock still. He removed his riding hat in an elegant sweep to his side and bowed his head in an obedience that could have been to an imaginary judge and crowd of spectators – or a gesture of respect to Bear himself. He walked back over slowly to me, reins loose now and Bear blowing quite hard with the exertion. Ridden dressage is deceptively demanding on horse and rider.

I tried not to sound too smug. 'Well, I know he's nothing compared with some of the big boys you will have ridden,

but wouldn't you agree he's not bad for an over-grown
native pony?'

'Yes,' said Alastair. 'I would have to agree.'

'Alastair, I will make you a promise. By the end of this
season you still may not be sold on Welsh Cobs. You may
not even like Bear and Blizzard but you will, I promise
you, you *will* respect them.'

These misgivings apart, everything at home and on the
yard was gliding along splendidly in our new well-oiled
routine. Sharon was proving a gem in her own way. Alastair was almost demented with her slowness to begin with,
but soon discovered it was pointless and hopeless to hurry
Sharon up or overload her. Best to set her each morning a
list of achievable tasks and allow her to plod through them
at her own sweet pace throughout the day. Alastair could
work faster and more effectively than two ordinary grooms
on his own, and with only two horses and a few ponies to
look after we were not under strength.

It was, however, very difficult for Alastair to be stuck
with a pupil to whom he could teach nothing theoretical.
The mysteries of feeding and the horse's digestive system,
and the names of the bones in the leg and foot, though
explained with patience and thoroughness to Sharon one
day, would all be mysteries again by the next. Her practical
work, however, was thorough and conscientious, and she
had three of the essentials for a groom: she was not afraid
of dirt, personal discomfort or hard work! She was also a
beautiful rider. Alastair admitted almost reluctantly 'That
girl is simply a natural: lovely seat, beautiful balance, kind
hands. Mind you,' he sounded slightly piqued, 'it's a good
job, because there is no way I could *teach* her to ride like
that!'

Sharon rarely completed a sentence without including
'You know' in it. Only she didn't pronounce it as two

words. Conversations went along the lines of: 'Do uno where the, uno, lead rope is?' or 'Have the horses had their, uno, feed yet?' It began to drive me nearly, uno, mad, particularly when Megan came home and asked what we were having for, uno, tea?

'Tolerance,' Richard would preach. 'Have a little patience; none of us are perfect – uno!'

Alastair's peculiarities were perhaps less annoying but no less amazing. He was a creature of habit and abhorred, above all else, dirt.

Horses are, if nothing else, dirty blighters, but he never objected to shovelling manure or clearing stable drains out. No, it was personal dirt – of body and of living space – that Alastair objected to. And so the little bedsit room, which in his predecessor's day had been a jungle of frilly underwear, Chinese paper parasols and half-naked Sylvester Stallone posters, underwent a transformation. The walls were adorned with a few sober watercolours and several antique embroidered texts – most of them biblical and of the 'Thou God Seest Me' variety. A selection of carefully arranged and lovingly nurtured pot plants arrived, and where two hundredweight of make-up had sprawled on top of the chest of drawers, a row of very uplifting books appeared. It was all very calm and serene. Monastic even.

After finishing a day's work that was strenuous by anyone's standards, Alastair would change into a tracksuit, get out his shiny red racing bike and pedal off for the odd ten miles or so. On his return he would head for the bathroom and emerge for his dinner immaculately though casually dressed, with clouds of wonderful fragrance still bubbling down the drainpipes.

After a dinner which, though elegantly consumed, wouldn't have disgraced an Irish navvy, he would politely excuse himself to his quarters to write up his diary, and read his Bible before retiring to bed around 9.30 pm. However early I got up and out on the yard, I would always be greeted by a freshly shaved, clean jodhpured, immaculately leather-booted Alastair already well through the morning's work.

I began to have serious doubts about him. Could anyone be this perfect? This non-smoking, non-drinking, non-swearing early to bed early to rise paragon? Some, if not all, of the mystery was explained when his mother came to collect him one weekend because his car was in for a service. She was, Alastair explained (I got the impression as a way of forewarning me), a very forthright lady, and a member of the Plymouth Brethren, a religious sect so radically to the right of mainline Quakerism as to make a normal gathering at a Friends' Meeting House seem like a den of iniquity and depravity.

Somewhat stunned by these revelations, and in my mind's eye trying Alastair out for size in an oatmeal habit, cowl and brown sandals, I awaited her arrival with bated breath. I conjured up a tall, sallow woman in a longish black dress with greying hair pulled back severely into a wispy bun.

The reality was therefore a surprise: an attractive lady in her mid-forties with classic soft country clothes, a short wavy hairstyle and just the right touch of makeup. In fact, I was feeling rather disappointed by the time we'd had a cuppa and they were installed in her smart red car for the drive home. She switched on the engine and wound down the window.

'What you need in your life,' she said firmly, looking me straight in the eye, 'is Jesus.'

As they rolled off down the back street I thought about the exceptional son she had produced, her radiant carefree face, and wondered if perhaps she might not be right.

3

Plod

At the beginning of the driving season, preparations reached a climax. Richard was driving the pair daily and initiating Alastair into the mysteries of driving and of being the groom or 'shot gun' on the back of the cross-country vehicle in the marathon.

The shot gun's job is to time the sections, and navigate and balance the back of the vehicle over often unbelievably rough terrain, across rivers and through the intricacies of hazards driven at speed. Richard stressed that he saw his job as getting the horses and front wheels around an obstacle; but that he relied upon his groom to get the back of the vehicle round and ensure that it kept upright and on all four wheels in the process. Our last groom, Chris, had been formidable on the back of a vehicle, lifting and swinging the seven hundredweight hunk of metal like a supermarket trolley while uttering blood-curdling Celtic encouragement to the horses. Alastair seemed to pick up the art very quickly, hanging nonchalantly on to the back grab rails, and shifting the rear end just the required few inches when Richard practised on our less than awe-inspiring home-made obstacles in the field.

'Isn't this quite what you expected?' I asked Alastair one day.

'Well the dressage is really quite fascinating and very

23

demanding, and driving a single and driving a pair of horses are totally new experiences for me . . .'

'But?'

'Well, it's not quite as exciting as I had expected it to be – the marathon part, the hazards I mean.'

'What hazards! Those paltry bits of post and rails and old pallets that Richard has built? Don't make your mind up until you've tried the real thing, till you pass your first finishing line on the back of that vehicle with everything still in one piece! Just see how you feel when you get off that back step after two hours of clinging on there for dear life.'

When the crescendo reached its fevered summit of painting and cleaning and polishing and packing, we were down to counting our departure for Brighton in days. Horses were clipped, manes hogged, tails banged and feet newly shod. Work harness was cleaned and oiled, show harness was polished and Brasso'd and all packed into large trunks, only to be unpacked the next day to be checked one more time by Alastair who was haunted with visions of arriving at the other end of the country for a full fortnight with three people, a mountain of equipment, two carriages and two horses, only to discover we'd left something vital like a trace or a carriage lamp behind.

The centre of Richard's attentions as we approached the crucial date was, surprisingly, not the horses, but Plod, his venerable and cantankerous horsebox. Newly resplendent in her Montan livery of red and grey and boldly lettered in black, she looked quite splendid. But looks, as they say, can be deceptive.

The sad but unavoidable fact was that she was just getting too old. Every year it seemed to take more and more effort, time and money to get the Old Girl roadworthy. Richard of course would have none of it. Grand old wagon; engine sweet as a nut, slow but sure. Alastair, having swiftly masked his initial shock on viewing what was to double as the transport for the horses and his home when away at shows, diplomatically said nothing.

At last, and horribly early one cold May morning, our little convoy headed out for a full fortnight away from home; a fortnight that would see a trial by fire for the Montan Carriage Driving Team at both Brighton and that most prestigious of all events on the equestrian calendar, the Royal Windsor Horse Show. Plod led the way with Richard driving, accompanied by myself wrapped in quilts and pillows in the faint hope of getting another few hours' sleep. The cobs swayed gently in her ample belly. The trailer containing the carriages (which would then convert to our living quarters on arrival at Brighton) bobbed behind like a rowing boat in the wake of a battleship. Bringing up the rear were Alastair driving Richard's transit van, with a cargo of hay, straw and feed for the fortnight, and Sharon, who was so wide-eyed and speechless with the excitement of it all, she couldn't even, well – 'uno'.

The horribly early start was because we had a horribly long journey ahead of us. About fourteen hours if the wind set fair for Plod. It didn't, of course, and we had our usual share of mishaps. It was still only five o'clock in the morning when we came to a halt on the slip road leading to the A1. A core plug had blown from the engine. The next couple of hours are best forgotten, but finally we were on our way again – until Richard discovered that the alternator had stuck, so that the battery was overcharging and the acid boiling.

'Bad luck,' my Great-aunt Meg would have muttered, 'always comes in threes.' So the remaining dreadful hours of the journey were spent with me perched miserably as near to the front of the cab seat as possible, longing to stretch out and snooze, but appalled at the thought of being engulfed by boiling acid from the battery behind my seat. I listened to my personal stereo until my head ached, went through the connecting door to check the horses every half hour or so; counted the little white posts alongside the motorway and nibbled biscuits, crisps and sweets until I felt quite sick. When we emerged unscathed through the Dartford Tunnel I began to dare to hope that we might just possibly make it. When we left the straight, but relatively effortless, monotony of the motorway and began labouring up and over the chalk Downs I was alternating between relief and hysteria. When we first saw our first AA sign saying 'Horse Driving Trials' and a big arrow I was praying, very, very hard. And when we rumbled slowly past the Lodge Gates and into the peace and security of Stamner Park, I was waving thumbs-up signs at Alastair out of the window like someone demented.

Trembling with a mixture of relief and cramped muscles, I landed very ungracefully on the grass beside the cab door.

'What's that?' I asked, 'that sort of hissing noise?'

'What hissing noise? I can't hear anything. Probably just the engine cooling down,' said Richard. 'You're getting neurotic about this wagon, that's your problem. Looking for trouble. Do something useful. Here, take our papers to the stable manager and get checked in. I'll get the ramp down.'

Bruised, I toddled off wearily, but on my return I couldn't help feeling slightly smug and thoroughly vindicated to see Plod lurching tipsily to one side, just as the last of the air went out of her front tyre. I could hear Great-aunt Meg chuckling.

Stamner Park in early May is one of my favourite places. Spring is about a month ahead of County Durham there, and the trees are laden with pink and white blossoms and the grass is a vivid emerald green when everything at home is still dull and dreary. The park itself, nestling within the magnificent mature woodlands surrounding it like a giant palisade, is a little jewel with its lovely old mansion house, church and duck pond. The welcome there from the organizers is always warm and genuine, the course well built and very demanding, and of course the excitement and exchange of gossip after the winter's close season is infectious.

After a quick cup of tea and a chance for horses and people alike to stretch their weary legs, the rapidly fading light spurred us on to get ourselves organized for the night. Bear and Blizzard were stabled under canvas at Plod's side in their familiar temporary stalls. With the long and awful journey behind us, spirits soon picked up, and by the time an evening meal had been consumed we were all ready to get a good night's sleep to restore ourselves for the next day.

That day, Thursday, saw the final preparations for the competition to come. Horses were shampooed from head to toe, tails plaited and tied up safely in old nylon stockings to keep them clean. Every last whisker on muzzles and chins was whisked away by Alastair's flying razor. Even the rough pieces of horn were sandpapered off hooves. The brass on the harness was given its last buff up before it was all hung behind protective blankets in the wagon and the carriage lamps polished until they shone like mirrors. When all this was done, Richard and Alastair set off for the first of many previews of the marathon and the hazards.

It was a very pensive and subdued Alastair that returned.

'You were right – it's nothing like Stanley Crook. To be honest,' he looked at me with just a hint of genuine apprehension, 'I'm not entirely sure how on earth they are going to get round some of these hazards – particularly by the routes Richard was talking about taking!'

'Don't worry yourself,' I assured him. 'Just have faith in the Boys and Richard, and concentrate on keeping the back of that cart on the ground.'

'All these weeks we've been preparing and waiting for the real thing. Now that it's here it doesn't seem real at all!'

'It'll be all right tomorrow, you'll see. When the bell goes and the horses set off down that centre line towards the judges, you'll see them for the first time for what they truly are – professionals. And they look splendid – they're a real credit to you Alastair, and to Sharon! They've never looked fitter or glossier or in better health.'

'Yes, well, they've come a long way from the hairy creatures I made acquaintance with in the New Year.'

'Tomorrow you'll see just how far, Alastair. Good night. Sleep well!'

The next day was the dressage, and our test put us into third place, but with only a few points between us and first place. The weather was so warm and lovely I decided we could eat outside that evening. No sooner had we consumed the first few mouthfuls than Sharon dropped her knife and fork in amazement. 'Oh, look!' she said. 'Look at that! It's beautiful, it's coming this way. Do you think it's going to, uno, park here?'

'It' was the longest, poshest, most shiny white and spanking new caravan I'd ever seen. Emblazoned along its side in elegant red and black lettering it proclaimed 'Montan Carriage Driving Team'. From the front window of the equally shiny bright and new Range Rover towing it, smiled Alan Robson.

'Yes, Sharon,' I replied. 'I very much think it is.'

'Where can I put this so it won't be in your way?' Alan yelled at Richard.

'Right there by the horsebox will be fine.'

Alan switched off the engine and climbed out. 'Phew.

Long journey that,' he said. 'It's taken us over six hours you know! Did you get down all right?'

'Oh, fine. Yes, fine. A minor hitch or two, that was all.' Richard said convincingly.

'I decided a mobile base would be the thing,' Alan was saying. 'I've got a couple of my directors coming down to join me for the event – to help look after the company guests and so on, and I'm sure it'll do them no harm to rough it in this with me for the weekend! Chris can't join us for this one, but she'll be flying down next weekend for Royal Windsor. Of course, I've got my guests in hotels for that one.'

I experienced my first sinking feeling of the day. Directors, company guests. People flying the length of the country. All to see a piece of the action. All expecting – what? To be impressed? Entertained? Exhilarated? All expecting *something* anyway.

We'd never had to consider anyone else but ourselves at events before, as our following supporters numbered one or two close friends on a good day. Victory was a personal triumph. Defeat a matter for private consolation. Amidst the feelings of near panic and a very real intrusion, guilt popped up its head and said, 'What did you expect? You wanted sponsorship. This is sponsorship: they pay, you come up with the goods. That's what it's all about you know.'

I forced my thoughts around until they squarely faced the spectre of despair and depression that had haunted us a few bleak months ago and I felt very ashamed of myself.

'You must be very tired and hungry after your long drive. We've just started our meal. Please join us – there's more than enough.'

Getting the horses ready for the marathon the next day with strange, curious, friendly eyes watching our every move was an odd feeling. Still it wasn't so bad. All my misgivings about bored society types gazing down their noses at us proved totally and thankfully wrong. The 'guests' were a delightful lot, all totally ignorant about the Carriage Driving bit, but excited about their day out and a chance to be in the very middle of all the horse lines. Some brought their wives, some brought their children. Spare wellies and boots were found for the ladies who'd arrived in high heels, thinking they'd be in a grandstand all day, not wandering about from hazard to hazard. Alan's director, Dennis, arrived and unloaded from his capacious boot an astonishing array of folding chairs, cocktail nibbles and an abundance of wine and beer, all of which he swiftly set out in the pavilion-like interior of the caravan awning. Then he produced another large cardboard box from the back seat.

'They arrived just in time!' he shouted to Alan. 'I thought we weren't going to get them!'

'Great!' replied Alan. 'Give them out then!'

And to my astonishment I was presented with a red and white American baseball-style cap blazoned with the company logo and 'Montan Carriage Driving Team'. This time, instead of feeling threatened by those words, I felt my first tingle of excitement, of having somehow moved into a higher league. The only person I knew who had a sponsor's hat was George Bowman, with his famous yellow and green 'Dalton Seasoning & Spices' logo. Young girl grooms had been known to offer more than their green wellies to get hold of one of those hats. Our very own hats; whatever next!

'Sorry about the jumpers, though; they didn't get back to us in time. They promised to send them direct to Royal Windsor, so we should have them for that.'

Hats! Jumpers! The horses standing patiently amongst all the hubbub in their beautiful new red and grey Montan rugs. One thing was sure now; it was over the top, and give them the best shot we had for Montan. They had done us proud and we had to try to do the same in return.

Suddenly Richard consulted his watch and announced, 'Right! Horses in.' Rugs were whipped off, harness buckles checked one last time by Alastair while Sharon, shaking with nerves, led them to the waiting vehicle. Her fingers suddenly all thumbs, I helped her to get them in and then Richard climbed up on to his seat while Alastair checked all three of his stopwatches for the umpteenth time.

'Haven't you forgotten something?' I enquired, handing Richard a virgin red and white cap.

'Ah yes.' Rather ruefully he passed me his beloved battered old tweed hat, and donned the new creation.

'You look very dashing. Good luck and . . . take care. And you too,' I smiled at Alastair as they rolled towards the start.

The next two hours were not easy. Normally I liked to do something mundane like clean harness or peel potatoes for supper to while away the first hour or so, then wander slowly to the first hazard in good time to see Richard through. And I definitely liked to be left well alone. I panic much better on my own. But now there were guests: I couldn't just closet myself in the trailer and shut the door.

A kindly face peered intently at me from beneath a Montan hat. 'You all right, love? You look quite pale and peaky.'

'Oh yes, I'm fine – it's just that I get a bit anxious when they go off, and I tend to stay that way until they get back!'

'Eeee, I'm sure you must, love. Listen, tell you what, I'll make you a nice cup of tea and you come and get your feet up a bit. You must be exhausted running after us lot.'

I suddenly blinked back to reality: this was a guest! I was supposed to be looking after *her*! I opened my mouth to protest.

'Now, not a word! Come on. I'll give you a hand with

all these cups an' all. I don't suppose you've got a dish-
washer in that little tin box you live in!'

'But you're missing all the excitement,' I protested.

'Oh, as long as we're there to see our team through –
that's all the excitement we want,' she replied happily.

An hour later saw me waiting by the first hazard. How
the horses came into the first one was always my measure
of how much steam they had left for the task ahead. If
they were full of attack and power, if their heads lifted and
ears pricked at the sight of their first challenge, then I knew
we were in with a good chance. If they were struggling
slightly with the rigours of the course, if heads were down
and necks stretched to ease tired muscles, then I knew
Richard would be more concerned about just nursing them
home safely.

Against the backdrop of the tall and splendid trees of
Stamner Park they crested the hill, ears pricked and nostrils
flaring; as soon as they crossed the penalty zone into the
first hazards they were into a gallop. Hooves pounding,
powerful quarters bending this way then that, checking
speed just long enough to negotiate a tricky bend with
millimetres to spare: accelerating swiftly to a gallop again
to gain precious seconds and coming back to a trot within
five strides on the other side of the penalty zone. My
anxiety was replaced with a glow of exhilaration and pride.
I urged silently, 'Go on lads! Go on!' before running as fast
as I could towards the next hazard.

At each hazard it was the same – they were on top form.
And at each hazard there was something novel happening;
a tightly knit bunch of red-and-white capped people, yelling and whooping and clapping the horses as they surged
through the exit gate. From a distance, for some absurd
reason, they reminded me of a rash of measles. Certainly
the infection of their excitement and pleasure was highly
contagious; I couldn't ever remember seeing a more
enthusiastic audience at an event, bustling and jostling at

each hazard, encouraging and commiserating accordingly with each and every competitor that came through. Whatever our sponsorship might bring us personally it was very satisfying to think that it might bring interest and good to the sport in general.

I became one more spot in the red and white rash at the finish to cheer the Boys home. As soon as they had passed the finish line, I rushed in to hug Richard and horses alike. Sharon, too, detached herself from the crowd and loped over to shower the Boys with pats and Polo mints. It was then I turned my attention to Alastair, still standing on the back step of the mud-splattered battle-wagon, head down and silent.

'All right?' I enquired.

He raised his head and smiled slowly and ruefully, his eyes bright. 'I take it all back,' he said. 'Every single thought and word about these horses. What they have done out there today is unbelievable. I've never seen such stamina, never seen horses prepared to give and keep on giving like that. Your horses, Carol – though I'm sure you don't need telling – are courageous and wise and I give them my undying admiration.'

'Thank you Alastair. Thank you very much.'

We were not the only people to have worked hard and long over the winter however, and the competition was very strong. We were still in third place after the marathon, though the gap between us and second place now didn't even merit one cone down the next day. One slip by our nearest rival and we would be second. A few unforeseen slips and we could even win.

'Aye, but there's many a slip between cup and lip!' Great-aunt Meg would have been unable to resist adding.

The cones they used for the final part of the competition were not of the usual type. These cones were virtually straight up and down instead of being triangular. This put no one at a disadvantage except Richard Smith, who just happened to drive an antique vehicle with large protruding hubs which meant he incurred a cricket score of penalties. But even Alan Robson could see that our back wheels could hardly squeeze through the gaps.

Back at our base, Richard had already turned what had seemed such a humiliation into a huge joke on himself and had everyone commiserating and laughing with him. I could see Alastair was still smarting, but our supporters stood by us to the end and, driving in to receive his 'also ran' rosette for eighth place, Richard got a bigger cheer than the winner.

'Never mind, love, damn shame – that's all. Not fair, that's what I say,' said my assistant washer-up as she prepared to leave. 'But we've had a smashing weekend, smashing it's been, and we think you and your horses are just lovely. I do hope we get invited again next year.'

Her sentiments were echoed by all the departing guests. Alan was delighted with the success of the weekend.

'It's not the winning that matters,' he said magnanimously, 'it's the taking part. Mind you,' he added in a slightly worried voice, 'they won't have those sort of cones at Windsor, will they?'

They didn't. They had the good old traditional yellow cones and amidst the pageantry, the splendour and the unmatchable atmosphere of Royal Windsor, Richard and the horses came fourth overall and the third British in a large international class. It was a splendid redemption of our performance at Brighton and from the cheers, whistles and waves from the company box as we flew past doing the final lap of honour, everyone concerned thought it was splendid too.

4

Right to the Very Top

The rest of the season fell into its usual hectic pattern of weeks or even fortnights on the road and then recovery periods at home. The results from the shows were mostly encouraging: a third at Holker Hall, a win at Islabank, Perth, and a superb performance at Floors Castle, Kelso, until the vehicle jack-knifed and snapped in two in a hazard. The Boys took a second place at Cirencester and also at Lowther, another event which had always been a bogey for us in previous years. Perhaps, I fervently hoped, we had finally laid the Lowther Curse.

Other things were not going so well however. Business at the shop hadn't been very healthy all year, and Richard would have been the first to admit that his heart and energies were more closely involved with his horses than with Ted's Shed. Now the business became fatally ill. The death-dealing blow was a government decision to cease the system of DHSS Giros for furniture and household effects for those on Supplementary Benefit. That trade, modest as it was, was our lifeblood.

Within a matter of weeks we were hardly taking any money at all, while the bills for the business – the rent, rates, phone, electricity and the transit van – all continued to arrive. By early September it was obvious we could sustain the losses no longer and would have to close.

What on earth we were going to do for a living we hadn't a clue, but Richard pointed out that with the National Championships now lying ahead of us our obligations really did lie with our sponsor. We should try and put our personal problems behind us, go all out for the Nationals and then decide what to do when the pressure was off. I cut all our household expenditure down to the bone and then to the marrow. It was a challenge for the first week or two: how little can I make a meal for today? How can I devise ways of saving even more electricity and fuel?

By the third week or so I was beginning to feel desperate about the whole situation. It was all very well Richard saying we would find a way after we'd concentrated on the Nationals – but how could I concentrate on *anything* when I literally didn't know where the next month's mortgage was coming from?

Richard was turned fifty, no spring chicken, with few qualifications to do anything other than be his own boss in the second-hand trade. I was a qualified teacher, it was true, but it was nine years since I'd taught anywhere and, even if anyone would have me, all the appointments for the coming school year would be filled.

The bitter irony was that although *we* had no security and no income, the horses were for once more secure than we were; they had their sponsorship. Until the end of the season anyway. And then what?

The weekend before the National Championships – normally delightful early autumn weather – was chill and grey and drear and therefore fitted my mood perfectly. I was wandering aimlessly around Crook market-place late on the Saturday afternoon. I was no longer challenged by the fact that my purse contained £15 to buy all the food and domestic requirements for three adults and a child for a week; I was thoroughly depressed by it. I had heard that last thing on a Saturday afternoon the supermarket cut the prices on any left-over fresh goods, hence my late shopping trip, when I bumped straight into a lady hurrying by with a basket.

'Carol?' It was Sandee Pattison, an old teaching friend I hadn't seen for a very long while. 'My goodness,' she was saying, 'things can't be as bad as all that – you look dreadfully down.'

'You'd better believe how bad things are,' I said miserably.

'How very, very strange to bump into you here, I was just talking about you at college yesterday and I was going to give you a ring tonight.' I had heard that Sandee now lectured part-time at Bishop Auckland Technical College.

'My head of department is pulling her hair out because they've just had the enrolment week and there are far more people wanting to do courses than she anticipated. She asked me if I knew any "Good old-fashioned cookery teachers" – those were her exact words – and I said I could only think of one, but I didn't know if she'd be interested because she was very busy with her horses and her husband's business.'

I needed work so desperately that I was indeed interested. 'What is it to teach?'

'Well, I do food and nutrition and a City and Guilds cookery course. Plus a bit of home management and community care. It's a bit of all sorts really. I could soon show you the ropes if need be. Look,' Sandee said, scribbling a number on to a scrap of paper, 'here's Miss Pickering's phone number. Give her a ring and see what she says.'

I was astounded to find myself signed up next Monday to do seven hours' teaching a week for a very nice hourly sum, beginning the day after we got back from the Nationals. It wasn't the solution to our problems, but it was a start; a chink of light along a badly illuminated path.

I was very grateful for even small mercies – and for friends like Sandee Pattison.

As suddenly as the season had come upon us, it was now coming to an end. We were about to do battle at the National Championships, a competition in which we had never come higher than third before.

This year we wanted to do better; we had our sponsors to think of. Though, after that disastrous journey to Brighton, Plod had literally not put a wheel wrong, we were pleased not to be faced with a gruelling journey to end the season. That year the competition was to be held at the Great Yorkshire Showground in Harrogate rather than at its traditional base in Windsor Great Park.

Harrogate is less than two hours from home and after their very brief journey, the horses were quite fresh and excited. Because of the early hour of our appearance in the dressage arena on the Friday morning, Alastair announced a very early ride out to be essential to settle them: at five am, to be exact.

Wanting to participate in the whole event as fully as possible, and also wanting to spare Sharon the ordeal of such an early start, I volunteered to ride out. Sharon was never exactly, uno, at her *best* in the mornings anyway.

There was one factor that I'm sure the organizers had overlooked when moving the event from Windsor to Harrogate. Harrogate is further north; a *lot* further north. By the end of September the days are noticeably shorter, and the weather noticeably sharper than down south.

When Alastair tapped on the trailer door the next morning it took me a few moments to realize that I was about to get up and ride a horse even though a strong, full, silvery moon was shining through the trailer window. I began to regret my noble offer of the previous day as I rolled out of bed. When I made contact with the trailer floor I totally regretted it! It was freezing cold; plumes of instantly distilled breath hung around me. Teeth chattering, I fumbled with the matches and lit first the gas ring for the kettle for tea and then the oven to get dressed in front of. I thought a lot of very uncharitable and unChristian things about Alastair for getting me up at such an unearthly hour.

Looking back, I would not have missed that morning's ride had I had to get up two hours earlier, or had it been twice as cold.

It had been over four years since Bear and I had been hunting. He had loved it, and had been ideally suited for the job; keen though sure-footed, a splendid but sensible jumper, with the stamina to go on to the day's end. In our hunting days we would be rising at just such an early hour in late September and hacking away into the sharp, beautiful autumn mornings. I valued not only the marvellous legacy of memories that hunting with Bear had left me, but also the superb character that it had left indelibly stamped upon him. I'm absolutely certain that his unflagging stamina, his zest for work and his courage in the face of challenge and adversity all stem from his education on the hunting field.

To assist with the smooth running of the show as well as to provide stirring ringside music, a detachment of soldiers was billeted at the far end of the ground. As I was fumbling with my girth, trying to tighten it with frost-nipped fingers, a lone bugle rang across the chill morning air, sounding Reveille. Bear's memory of pre-dawn activity, sharp autumn mornings, the clear notes of a horn, told him that, obviously, we were going hunting! The prospect apparently delighted him, and he danced and jingled with impatience as I tried to mount.

'I've a feeling he's going to be a bit full of himself, Alastair!' I said.

'Nice steady work, an hour's fast walking, should settle them down,' he replied.

We headed through the still slumbering horse lines, the cobs' feet ringing on the sparkling frosty tarmac. The only sign of life was from the night-watchman who rushed out of his hut near the perimeter fence, adjusting his hat and waving his torch. We showed him our badges, assured him we were not kidnapping anyone's horses and he swung open the gates to allow us access to the exercise field that lay beyond. A flush of pink light appeared on the tree-lined horizon ahead as we walked the horses briskly along the road. Within minutes a pale glow was diffused over the dark sky and in that eerie half-light we could see a dense mist, swirling and silvery, lying across the surface of the grass.

We reined in the horses and just stood at the edge of the grass to drink in the dawn. While tendrils of mist licked around the horses' feet and gossamer banners of their warm breath hung suspended in the freezing air, the fire in the sky deepened from pink to scarlet and from behind the trees the glowing disc of the sun appeared. Behind us, the moon had no intention of surrendering her hold on the sky easily or quickly. And so we stood there, at the fulcrum of day and night, with the flat crimson disc of the sun almost defied by the cold white power of the moon; so magical was it that, human and horses alike, we were stunned into immobility by the beauty and splendour. As in every enactment of this battle since the first day of creation, the dark slowly, reluctantly retreated and the light, triumphant, filled the sky. Still awed, we moved forward.

Now, reflecting the warm tones of the sky, the silvery mist had turned to pink and gold candyfloss which fluffed and swirled around the horses' knees as they walked. The cold clear air seemed to amplify the smallest sound and so the jingle of curb chains rang like bells around the meadow and every exhalation the horses made was like a tiny breath of wind. Then, across the still air, pure and clean and sweet, the notes of the bugle sounded once more. The sound hit Bear almost as a blow; he stopped dead, tense and quivering, the sharp staccato notes meaning only one thing to him – it was time to run, run as fast and as hard as he knew how to run. His excitement was intense, his disappointment when I held him back rather than urging him on forward, frustrating. His neck was set now, crested and hard, my every attempt to settle him to a walk or even a steady trot meeting more and more resistance. For perhaps the first time in our long acquaintance I sensed that I was about to be faced with outright disobedience. Bear's breath was coming in short snorts and he clamped his bit firmly in his mouth so that any messages I was trying to send down the reins were totally futile. He was almost cantering on the spot – with virtually no forward momentum at all – a movement which would take some years to master at the Spanish Riding School. His excitement was obviously infectious, and Blizzard too was thoroughly agitated. 'Discretion,' Alastair shouted as he wheeled round his prancing, snorting mount, 'is the better part of valour! Let's go!'

It was a mental rather than a physical release that I gave Bear, and yet within a few strides he had accelerated into a thundering purposeful gallop. He felt as if he was bursting with joy at just being alive, at being fit and well on this most glorious of mornings.

I was not in control; I was only a passenger as he plunged full stretch across the field. It was dangerous, it was reckless. With the mist underfoot there was no way I could judge the terrain, or even suggest a course for him to follow, but I felt charmed in some way in those magical moments. He did not gallop across that field, he flew. On top of the sinuous, swirling mists he flew as Pegasus across the top of the clouds. I didn't want it to end, not ever, this rare and unrepeatable sharing of the true power and beauty of an animal whom, most of the time, I had the audacity to think *I* controlled. But the far edge of the field drew nearer, the outlines of horseboxes and reality became discernible.

Reluctantly but graciously Bear slowed his pace to a steady canter. As the blood ceased singing in my ears and the sharp wind ceased cutting at my face I heard for the first time the thud of Blizzard's hoofbeats behind me. As positively as he had taken control, Bear gave it back; the reins lay responsive in my hands once more, his bit featherlight in his mouth. With the gentlest of pulls he obediently slowed to a complete halt.

Alastair drew up beside me. 'Not quite according to plan, I'm afraid,' he said.

'No,' I agreed, 'but I wouldn't have missed that for the world. And who knows – it might have whetted their appetites for the dressage.'

We will never know whether it was the superb billiard-table surface of the arena, or a long pre-ordained karma or simply good luck, but later that morning the Boys drove the best dressage test they had ever driven, and finished second by only a marginal two points to Christine Dick, our previously untouchable friend and rival in the pairs class. So now it was the marathon – and the heat was well and truly on.

We knew that Christine would be going all out to increase her lead, that she was unused to competition so hot on her heels. We knew too that she would be aware that one stupid mistake, one hold-up in a hazard, and she might fail to secure the title. A little passionate voice inside me kept whispering that perhaps this might be the day our Boys finally made it right to the very top!

One of the problems about a marathon is that it is impossible to see everyone in any particular class go through every hazard. Richard commenced his marathon before Christine, and, thanks to the layout of the hazards, which ran down the central backbone of the course, I was able to see him through them all. The horses were on top form. The wings that had carried them over the rolling morning mist the previous day, now carried them through the hazards with amazing power and alacrity.

I watched with heart-stopping anxiety and excitement as they twisted and surged their way through – I wasn't truly interested in seconds and scores and penalty points. I only knew that they were giving of their very best and that I could ask no more of them.

Christine was only a couple of competitors behind Richard and for once, instead of racing off to greet our horses at the finishing line, I simply couldn't resist the urge to stay and watch her tackle the hazards. After all, this was the top lady whip in the country, a lady who was driving a team of ponies by the age of seventeen and who had thrilled the nation's 'Horse of the Year Show' viewers with her speed and daring in the scurry-driving world.

'Come on, Pavlov, come on, Peanuts!' was the cry no horse-mad teenager of that period would ever forget. In the carriage-driving trials world her pedigree was no less staggering; she had seven National Championship wins to her name, and appearances at World level with both teams and pairs of horses. She was a lady after my own heart when it came to horses as well; no chopping or changing for Christine Dick. No trying and discarding horses because they didn't come up with the goods in the first season. Her chestnut Welsh Cob crosses were the age and size of Bear at around 15.1 hands high and about fourteen years old. They had wonderful, stirring, resonant names that tripped off the tongue like half a pack of foxhounds – Victor and Viking, Venture and Vivid. They were superb and so was she. But, my God, the little whisper tingled inside, she would have to be going some today to beat Richard Smith, Conwy Blaze and Cornsay Blizzard.

The second hazard was built on a camber and the ground within the twenty-metre penalty zone was hard and deeply rutted by this stage of the competition. Even though she was the opposition, it was difficult not to thrill to Christine's horses as they plunged into the hazards. One of the advantages her slightly lighter cross-bred cobs always had over ours was their phenomenal rate of acceleration; they could leap into a gallop from a standstill in a few strides. They entered the hazard at just such a break-neck speed, checked in time to negotiate the elements in the middle and Chris turned them for the dash out. However, this hazard was built so that the exit gate did not line up straight with the last element.

'Ha!' yelled Christine and, foam flying, her horses leapt forward and her husband John on the back and the referee on the front were nearly dislodged with the acceleration. Christine, perhaps realizing the exit gate was farther along the perimeter of the penalty zone than she had imagined, began to pull round in a sweeping arc. The ground was quite simply too hard, and the camber too steep, for such a manoeuvre at such speed. One second the carriage was surging forward. The next, the momentum was sideways as it slid down the hill, a slide which in itself could have been corrected had not the wheels suddenly come up against a solid, compacted rut. Seven hundredweight of metal travelling at speed came to an abrupt stop. The effect was catastrophic.

In horror we all watched as the carriage tipped sideways. John Dick and the referee were flung off first, and landed relatively intact. But Christine, perhaps anchored longer by her hold on the reins, was tossed like a rag doll through the air before landing head first on that concrete-hard ground.

The frightened horses, driverless and directionless, took

off in great alarm with the upturned vehicle bumping and clattering behind them, but the large crowd of spectators and fellow competitors caught them before they damaged themselves. For Christine the damage was already done and, helpless and stunned, we watched the flashing blue lights carry her and an ashen John to hospital.

An unhappy silence hung over the horse lines that evening. Anxious messages sped here and there: severe blow to the head; suspected fracture; very unwell.

On the score board I gazed intently at the little figure '1' next to Richard's name. It would have meant the whole world to me if there hadn't been the little letter 'R' next to Christine's name. 'Retired.' What a totally stupid word to describe what had happened that day.

In the obstacle driving the following day I prayed just as hard for Richard to get a clear round as if he needed every single point to hold on to his win. In fact he was so far ahead now he could have had several cones down, and still have won comfortably. But I didn't want him to win comfortably – I wanted him to win in style, to win as convincingly as possible.

Already, not unkindly, and perhaps not totally without justification, the rumbles had started: 'Only a win by default . . .'; 'Might have been different if Chris hadn't tipped up . . .'

'. . . and that completes the course, with a double clear for Richard Smith driving the Montan Logo Carriage Driving Team pair. A double clear, and Richard keeps his place to become the new National Champion! Congratulations to Richard and of course to his sponsors, who must be thrilled . . .'

We had done it. Alan Robson's sponsorship had enabled us to become National Champions of 1986.

Tears of joy and relief and sorrow welled up in my eyes.

Our sport was a battle: a battle that was very dangerous beneath its veneer of excitement, pageantry and tradition. It could just as easily have been Richard lying in that hospital as Christine. The spectators would ooh and aahh, and then go back home. How many of them, I questioned myself almost bitterly, had any idea of the endless hard work, the determination and the sheer peril that went behind the competition they had just witnessed?

So why did we subject ourselves, our horses, our very lives to it? Without hesitation, the answer came back: because of the satisfaction that comes from determination, because of the exhilaration that goes hand in hand with peril, because for us and our horses it *was* very life itself. The mountain had to be climbed – simply because it was there.

The bronze Famous Grouse trophy was magnificent, the size of the bottle of whisky obscene, and the military band was letting rip with *Congratulations* as the carriage containing Richard, myself and Alastair flew round the arena on our personal lap of honour, and a wildly ecstatic rash of measles in the grandstand clapped and whistled and stomped in approval. In those moments the euphoria was genuine, the joy and satisfaction deep and glowing.

No sooner had we returned to base and Richard had seen the horses unhitched and put away, than he quickly changed out of his top hat and jacket and asked for the car keys. 'Where are you going? I think Alan's got all his guests and friends coming over to tackle that bottle of whisky,' I asked.

'I'll only be an hour or so. There's something I must do first, or there'll be no enjoyment for me tonight. They mightn't even let me in.'

The wheel of life came round full circle in that moment.

'You realize where Christine is of course?' I asked quietly.

'Yes, Harrogate Accident Hospital.'

I remembered then the hours I had lain in that very same hospital, hours when my whole life had seemed as shattered as my pelvis and my hip. I remembered my lifeline, my sanity, held together only by the frequent visits from Richard Smith, who seemed capable of charming his way past both ward sisters and hospital visiting regulations. I handed him the keys. 'I'm sure you'll find a way to get in somehow.'

I sat for a long time after he'd gone, just staring at the magnificent bronze sculpture of the pair of grouse that was ours to keep for the next year.

Till the next time.

What, I wondered with a mixture of excitement and apprehension, would the next twelve months bring? On whose table would those birds so quietly roost one year from now?

For the first time ever I was spared the inevitable anticlimax that follows the end of a season – I was simply too busy. Nine years out of the teaching profession left me a trifle apprehensive to say the least, and for my first week at Bishop Auckland Technical College I didn't know if I was on my head or my heels. But despite my new job, we were still not as secure as we needed to be: Richard had no employment whatsoever.

I pointed out that the good Lord had not found us a sponsor, brought us safely through an enormously successful season and provided my job at the college just to let us and the horses flounder now. Richard, I regret to say, had more faith in worldly powers than in the Almighty's, and he could certainly see no connection between the two when Alan Robson again came to the rescue.

The season had been so successful, the Company's guests so delighted and the feedback so positive, that they had decided to continue the sponsorship for a further year. Recognizing, however, that the horses were not going to prosper if their driver didn't have a living, Alan offered Richard employment in the New Year as a Transport Manager with one of his companies.

We still had the problem of three months on half rations to weather, but knowing for certain that calmer waters lay ahead we were not unduly despondent and Alastair came up with a suggestion to help alleviate the problem. As it was the horses' rest period and we would be wanting to cut back on shoeing and feed bills by doing as little as possible until Christmas, he was really going to be surplus to requirements. How would it be, he suggested, if he left our employment and looked for some teaching work for a couple of months or so, returning to us to start preparations for the new season in the New Year? It sounded an admirable and sensible plan and yet I couldn't help feeling a sense of loss, a sense of the withdrawing of standards and organization from our lives as the gleaming little Panda car bumped down the back lane with Alastair's cherished pot plants waving goodbye merrily from the back seat.

We would not see Alastair, or indeed his like, upon our little yard again. Richard said I was being ridiculous, but my foreboding was painfully true. Four days before he was due to recommence work, Alastair phoned to say he had been offered the teaching job of a lifetime: in America. It was too good an offer to refuse . . . he felt very badly about letting us down . . . was sure we would find someone very suitable . . .

Richard was quite devastated. In the few short months Alastair had been with us, my middle-aged, down-to-earth husband had developed a great liking for this elegant, talented young man. He had respected and even come to depend upon him far more than he had realized. He had built his plans for the coming season around their working partnership.

Now those plans would have to be changed – and quickly. For we were now into 1987 and without a professional groom. Two things made this state of affairs very urgent: firstly my so-called 'part-time' job seemed to make enormous inroads into my time and therefore my contributions on the yard. Secondly, 1987 would see the second World Pairs Driving Championship in Reisenbech, Germany. And we had every intention of being there.

While Richard still smarted and hurt from his loss – of plans? Of a male ally? Of loyalty? – I, ever practical, began the hunt for a new groom. Racking my brains for inspiration, and trying to save the advertisement costs in *Horse and Hound*, I decided the best course of action was the grapevine. Who better, I decided, to know what was going on in the carriage driving world than Stella Hancock, wife of the Chairman of the Horse Driving Trials Group, the same Hancocks who had so generously provided us with the third horse for the World Championships in 1985?

'Oh, my dear, how devastating,' sympathized Stella over the phone. 'But now, don't despair, I think I might know just the gal that could do for you.'

'The Gal' was not an AI, or a well-qualified rider, but she had helped Stella with her disabled driving group. Stella knew she had some driving experience, and she also thought she was at a loose end at the present. Of course, I could place adverts nationwide and pick and choose and take my time, but . . .

I wrote down phone numbers gratefully and within a week a large, well-built girl with curly ginger hair and freckles was ensconced in the room that had once held Chris Morris-Jones's Sylvester Stallone posters and, more recently, Alastair's potted plants and Bible. Her name was Heather Baldwin and she came from Norfolk.

Sharon, now in her second year of YTS, and Heather seemed to hit it off all right, though Heather was not the knowledgeable, authoritative figure Alastair had been.

There were other, major changes. Shaking his head miserably and cradling a brake pipe that was rotten right through, Richard had to admit that, this year, his annual overhaul on Plod just wasn't going to make her roadworthy. Montan said they had a wagon they could let us have which would convert into a horsebox. Richard was very grateful but, alas, nothing could really replace Plod. When a huge breakdown wagon appeared to take her for scrap, Richard had already fled our yard for the day, totally bereaved at the loss of his old friend.

I sympathized to a point, but just how did one perform the last rites over a nine-ton lump of metal and wood? Megan and I watched with interest while they hooked up the towbar to her front, and very reluctantly she creaked and rolled forward from her long and final winter slumber. The man at the wheel was obviously trying out the various knobs and switches before he reached the road with her and as I viewed her broad beam rolling ponderously down the back street, more moved than I liked to admit, her right back indicator began slowly and feebly to flicker on and off.

'Oh, Mummy!' cried Megan, clutching my arm and pointing. 'Look at Plod! Look Mummy, look, she's not dead! She's winking goodbye!'

Stupid, useless tears slid down my cheeks in farewell: not perhaps to a friend, but to an era.

After a respectful but brief period of mourning Richard appeared home from work one evening at the wheel of Plod's successor. This one was a male of the species (how *do* you tell the sex of a horsebox?) and went by the name of 'Teg'; a fact that was emblazoned upon his number plate.

5

Bobby Dazzler

One long cherished plan of mine did develop really rapidly in the spring of 1987, though perhaps I didn't make the connection immediately when the diminutive figure of Brenda Harrison turned up on my doorstep. She wanted some advice, she said as she wiped first her callipered boots and then the ends of her sticks on the doormat, about a pony she had just purchased. She lived not far from us and had regularly seen me sail by with Bear in the trap, and had decided that, at last, she saw a way in which she could participate in an equestrian sport. Having, I soon discovered, the heart of a lion in the body of a very small woman who walked with sticks and callipers, she had set about doing it the hard way: breaking in a pony to drive herself. A few hair-raising outings and a pile-up in a ditch had persuaded her that perhaps she should get a more experienced animal to begin with and after much searching she now felt she had found the right one, a black Welsh pony called 'Glint'.

Would it be possible, she enquired, for the pony to come and stay with us for a little while so that both the pony and she could have a little instruction and help?

Within a week Glint was installed and Brenda's driving career had begun.

It didn't take Brenda long to get her eye on Bobby. 'Oh! I see you already have a Welsh pony here.'

Bobby was the diminutive palomino Welsh pony that roamed around our fields and occasionally came to the gate to say hello, but otherwise went about his own business.

'That's a very nice pony you know: why isn't he doing something useful?

'Well he isn't ours for one thing – he's just lived here for a couple of years and to be honest we really haven't had time to do anything with him. And with him being so ill . . .'

'Ill? He doesn't look ill to me. He's as fat as butter; what was supposed to be wrong with him?'

'I think you'd better come into the house and have a cup of tea,' I said, 'and I'll tell you the whole story.'

It had begun when I'd opened the back door one day in 1985 to find a gentleman standing there, hat in hand and peering at me through thick spectacles.

'Mrs Smith?' he enquired politely.

'Yes?' He moved uncomfortably from one foot to the other scribing little circles on the ground with the tip of his walking stick. I wasn't quite sure what to say: 'I'm sorry Mr . . . er?'

'Oh dear me, Nicholson – George Nicholson,' he said, rapidly extending his hand and nearly dropping his hat in the process.

'What can I do for you?'

'It's my pony.'

'Ah.'

Now I'm not in the habit of asking total strangers into the house, but a sharp late autumn wind was blowing up the alley that separated us from the somewhat disreputable public house next door and he had no overcoat on, only a well worn RAFA blazer. 'Why don't you come in Mr Nicholson and have a cup of tea in the kitchen where it's warm and you can explain the problem to me.'

Thankfully, he came indoors, peering intently through his spectacles and using his stick to feel the way. I realized that his sight must be poor indeed. Chasing an indignant cat off the armchair by the stove, I piled on a few more logs and put the kettle on.

Over tea and relaxed in the glowing warmth, the tale unfolded of how, that summer, he had finally realized a long-held dream to own a pony of his own. His deteriorating eyesight meant that car driving was no longer possible, but he had thought that if he could get a little horse and cart then he could potter around the by-ways with his wife to his heart's content. It was while on holiday in Wales that they had, by chance, come across a local auction and there in the ring stood the pony of his dreams: a sturdily built stunning little palomino who rejoiced in the name of 'Bobby Dazzler'. Never had a pony been so well named, George enthused. His coat was the colour of ripe apricots and his mane and tail were silvery white. He was three years old and fully registered.

Bobby was brought back to County Durham and installed in a rented field, but now, with winter approaching, the farmer wanted the field back.

'So you see, Mrs Smith, I'm desperate. I was told you had grazing you might rent. I would gladly pay whatever you require.'

He had indeed finished on a note of near desperation, his eyes full of hope behind the thick lenses of his glasses, and I remembered a very similar situation from ten or more years before, when I had just bought a gangly young Welsh Cob, also on pure impulse. My first very own horse, my life's ambition fulfilled. I remembered having nowhere to keep him but a pocket handkerchief of a garden and the joy and relief when a kindly neighbouring farmer had agreed to graze him.

Here was a chance to help somebody standing at that very same crossroads. We had seventeen acres of rough but serviceable pasture, a set of ramshackle buildings and only a pair of Welsh Cobs and my daughter's diminutive Shetland Pony rattling round the place.

'When would you like to bring him, Mr Nicholson?'

And so Bobby arrived and, after a brief inspection by the cobs and a swift punch-up with the Shetland pony, settled in remarkably quickly. He had wintered well but in the spring it was obvious that something was radically wrong. Despite regular and good feeding, a field shelter and stabling in bad weather, there was no way Bobby could be described as a dazzler any more. He was more like a walking hat-rack. The deterioration had been very rapid and we had tried everything obvious like worming and vitamin supplements, but when the rush of lush spring grass failed to interest him while the others attacked it like demented lawn-mowers and we noticed a distinctly unpleasant fishy smell on his breath, we decided a vet was needed.

George said he would get his vet. I said it would be simpler to get our vet.

No, said George, not wanting to cause us any more bother, he had had a local vet out to his dog when he'd been at death's door and he'd been marvellous. Admittedly it had been years ago, but he'd phone and see if he would call.

When the vet arrived I wondered just exactly how many years previously he had attended George's dog and how long it was since he had dealt with a pony. Or anything else come to that.

He had a broad Scottish accent and rolled towards the stable on legs that were somewhat unsteady. How much this was due to advanced arthritis and how much to that favourite Scottish cure, of which he reeked strongly, I couldn't tell. In a sonorous rumble he explained he was really retired now, but being called upon by a faithful client he felt it was his bounden duty to come.

He examined Bobby briefly, listened to his heart and then pondered before delivering his judgement in tones reminiscent of Dr Cameron in *Dr Finlay's Casebook*.

'Aye fear there is nothing aye can do.'

'Pardon?' I couldn't believe my ears.

'The kindest thing ye can do, my dear, would be to phone the knacker man.'

'Why, what's wrong with him?' I was horrified.

'Heart failure.'

'Heart failure? But he's only three years old! How can he have heart failure?'

The vet lowered his gaze over his half-moon spectacles and said with great finality and dignity, 'Congenital heart failure.'

'But the smell!' I protested, still not convinced, 'what's that terrible smell caused by?'

'It'll be liver failure. Aye. Oh Aye. All part of the general deterioration. Puir wee soul. Aye.' He wrote something on a piece of paper. 'Here's the number of the knacker man. Best thing, aye, the best thing.' And he rolled solemnly back to his waiting car and driver.

Breaking this news to George and his wife Marjorie was one of the hardest things I'd ever had to do. George was in tears, Marjorie was in tears and I was in tears. But they pitifully implored me to make all the necessary arrangements and I went home with a heart like lead to make the only necessary phone call.

Mr Miller, the knacker man, was booked for the next day.

When Richard came home, his reaction was of disbelief, then of anger. 'I don't believe it.'

'Neither do I! But that's what he says and there's no doubt Bobby's failing fast. Best to end his suffering; he won't eat at all now you know.'

'Won't eat or *can't* eat?' Richard said emphatically.

'What do you mean?'

'Come with me; I've been thinking about this all day.'

We went across to Bobby's stable, and Richard offered Bobby a bucket with a few pony nuts in the bottom. Bobby's eyes did seem to flicker hopefully when he saw the food and he put his muzzle in the bucket and pushed the nuts around before taking his head out and turning miserably away. It was pathetic.

'Get some wet sugar-beet pulp,' Richard ordered.

'But why . . .?'

'Just get some!'

This time, when offered the damp sugar beet, the pony sloshed it vigorously around the bucket before giving up.

'Go and make it wetter,' Richard said excitedly. 'Much wetter – liquid in fact!'

When I placed the slushy wet mass under Bobby's nose he nuzzled it briefly before beginning to suck it desperately into his mouth, sucking and sucking until the bucket was nearly empty.

'He's eaten it!' I screeched. 'Well, drunk it!'

'There's nothing wrong with that pony's heart; it's something to do with his mouth. It's not that he won't eat, the poor beggar can't eat! Why didn't we realize it earlier? I'm off to phone Mr Peacock. And cancel Miller!'

Mr Peacock, a long-suffering gentleman who had been Richard's vet for many years and knew that if Richard pushed the panic button something really was wrong, was summoned and arrived within the hour.

He carefully poked and prodded around the pony's jaw and over his cheeks – something Bobby didn't enjoy, but he was too weak to put up much of a struggle. When the vet tried to prise open Bobby's mouth it was like trying to force open a door with very rusty hinges and obviously caused Bobby great pain. Once open, a smell not unlike a Calcutta sewer on a hot day wafted out into the stable.

'Dear God, that's terrible,' Richard gasped. 'What's wrong with him?'

Mr Peacock poked and prodded a little more before letting the trembling, struggling pony shut his mouth.

'Sinuses,' he said simply. 'Massively infected, blocked sinuses. The whole of the left cheek is infected and inflamed to a dreadful degree. The hinge of his jaw is virtually locked. It must be agony to try to chew and the infection is draining into the back of his throat. Hence the smell. I'll give him a shot of antibiotics. He will need more, daily for a while. The shots are just intra-muscular and I'll leave them for you to do, Richard. That should clear it up, but it may need draining eventually. Keep him in, give him plenty to drink and keep on with the sloppy food until he can manage to chew.'

All week I sterilized the needle and syringe and prepared the injections – but that was as far as I went. I had a particular horror of needles being stuck into me and so didn't relish the thought of sticking them into anyone else. Richard had to do the actual business.

Bobby's face began to come up like a balloon, the swelling actually forcing his eye shut. But Mr Peacock assured us on the phone that this at least meant the infection was on the move, away from his throat and jaw. Certainly he could open his mouth a little now, managing wet mash type feeds, but there was still no way Bobby could eat hay.

Then came the weekend when Richard was helping with a driving event in the Midlands. He left very early on the Saturday morning, promising to be back late evening, but at tea-time I got a phone call to say things had dragged on longer than expected, it was a long drive back and friends had invited him to stay the night. In other words, he was having a jolly good time and didn't feel like coming home. Only after I put the phone down did I remember Bobby's injection.

I knew that Bobby couldn't miss out on his injection that

night and was fighting back waves of panic, trying to organize needles, syringes and so on, when through my back door came my old, dear friend Maria who had just happened to descend for one of her once-in-a-blue-moon visits. However, although old and dear, she was also sophisticated, well dressed, largely un-country and totally un-horsy.

'My God!' she gasped, viewing simultaneously a whisky bottle and a very large hypodermic syringe. 'What do you do? Take it intravenously these days?'

I giggled slightly hysterically.

'Hello! And no, stupid! It's Dutch courage actually. I've got to go out and stick this in a sick pony and, well, I've never done it before. It would be a tremendous help if you could hold the pony for me?' I ended the sentence on an upward, wheedling inflection. She blanched visibly and rocked on her high heels.

'I'd better have one of those too then!'

Garbed in spare wellies and waxed jacket, both of which she wrinkled her nose up at, we set off for the stable. When I'd last seen Bobby his face had been grotesquely swollen. Looking over the stable door I saw the swelling had gone down rapidly. Too rapidly.

As I got closer I soon saw why: Bobby's cheek had literally burst. There was a ragged hole behind his eye, about four inches long, from which green and yellow pus trickled, mingled with a little blood. The smell was indescribable. Maria uttered a high shriek, 'What's happened to his *face*?'

'It would appear to have burst,' I answered quite matter-of-factly – this was a remarkable feat considering my pulse rate had trebled and my mind was racing. If I phoned the vet this time on a Saturday night it would have to be pretty urgent. What could he do if he came out anyway? Probably just clean Bobby's face up and give him his injection. Mr Peacock had said the infection might have to be drained.

Well, it appeared that nature had taken things into her own hands. I couldn't call him out just to clean Bobby up. Surely I could do that myself? Couldn't I?

Next to needles the thing I pass out over most easily is blood.

'You're going to have to give me a hand to clean him up,' I said softly, but all that came from my friend was a low moaning sound as she clutched the stable door.

'Look!' I said, getting psyched up for the task ahead. 'He's in great pain and in a terrible mess, we can't leave him like this! Don't be such a wimp!' This meant that now I couldn't be seen to be a wimp either. 'All I want you to do is hold him while I give him the jab. OK?'

The injection that had been the focal point of my horror for the entire evening was suddenly so insignificant that I swabbed his neck, banged it vigorously with the back of my hand, stuck the needle in, attached the syringe and depressed the plunger with impressive professionalism.

Maria seemed impressed anyway, which boosted my confidence a little for the task ahead. Feeling more in control of the situation I headed back to the house for supplies. I quickly returned with boiled water and disinfectant in a large bowl, some gauze and a couple of towels. I had thought about the whisky bottle, but decided we might need it more later on.

Maria was still bravely hanging on to Bobby's headcollar, desperately trying to keep her hands away from the red, yellow and green trickles that were dripping from his muzzle. But when I applied the first piece of lukewarm gauze to Bobby's face, he squealed in pain and wrenched himself from Maria's hands. I don't know who was the more frightened.

'You said he wouldn't move!' Maria shot at me, almost in tears.

I had to calm Bobby down, take some of his pain away and keep him immobile till I got him cleaned up. But how?

Of course! The answer came rapidly. The twitch! When I wanted Bear – who was paranoid about having his ears clipped – to stand still while the unpleasant business was done, how did I render him co-operative and immobile? The twitch.

From the relative security of the stable doorway, Maria watched in absolute horror while I twisted then tightened a loop of rope attached to a stout piece of stick around Bobby's top lip. Indignantly she demanded, 'What on earth are you doing? That's terrible! That's cruel! The poor creature is in enough pain already!'

'Endorphines,' I replied, giving one more twist before beginning rhythmically to rock the twitch.

'Endo whats?' she asked.

'Endorphines; nature's own tranquillizing and pain-killing system. They'll be flooding his bloodstream in a minute or so.'

'Oh come on! Pull the other one. Look, Carol, I can't stand much more of this. I'm sorry, I'm not into animal liberation or anything, but I can't watch you torturing that creature. I think I'd better go.'

'No wait! Honestly, believe me! I used to think that about twitching until the vet explained, now look, watch him; his eyes are drooping closed, his ears are relaxed, he's not tense anymore!'

She sidled reluctantly back into the stable, and actually ventured to touch his neck.

'See! He's not afraid anymore!'

'Umm . . .'

'OK? So. You hold the twitch and rock it and I'll start cleaning him up.'

'Me! I . . .'

'*Don't* start that again.'

When I dabbed at Bobby's cheek experimentally he never flinched. Encouraged, I dabbed a little harder. Thick viscous yellow stuff spurted out, then more, then even

more. Then green stuff and more yellow stuff; then some
blood-stained stuff.

'I'm going to faint!' came a little voice.

'No you're not,' I hissed through clenched teeth. 'If anyone's going to faint it's going to be me: I deserve it for
cleaning up this lot!'

Eventually, when I had run out of gauze and towels and
water and at least a pint of multi-coloured noxious grot
had been coaxed and cleaned from Bobby's face, we took
the twitch off.

'I WANT' (the 'want' was definitely in capitals). 'I WANT
another whisky, a hot bath and a bed for the night – in
that order,' snapped my friend. And then, less harshly, 'Do
you think he'll get any better now?'

'Get better?' I was grinning. 'He's already got better.
Look! He hasn't done that for weeks now!'

And, freed from the pressure and pain in the joint in
his jaw, our patient had already began – carefully but
deliberately – to munch on a small mouthful of hay.

This however was not the end of Bobby's plight because,
although he did get better, he then got worse again. The
infection never went to the joint in his jaw again, nor
stopped him from eating, but every six weeks or so the
sinuses would block and infect and up would come his
face. It became obvious that he couldn't live on constant
antibiotics and so a simple mechanical solution was found.
Mr Peacock came and provided Bobby with a third 'nostril'
– a neat little hole which he drilled into Bobby's left cheek-
bone under local anaesthetic. This allowed the sinuses to
drain more quickly and effectively, thus preventing block-
age. The system worked more or less automatically. The
only regular care that was needed was to clear up the area
of any scabs or crusts about once a week. After all, ponies
have great difficulty in picking their own noses.

*

'So how long ago did all this happen?' enquired Brenda.

'Oh a couple of years ago,' I replied.

'And what happened to George's dream? You know – the pony and trap bit.'

'Well, I think he's been a little anxious that Bobby's not very strong . . .'

'Not strong? He's like a little tank I'd say!'

'. . . and then of course, over the winter it's a long hard walk for George up to this hill top. Mind you, come the spring he'll be up every day if only to give Bobby a carrot and check his nose. He did mention last summer how he has got the chance of a little trap if he needs it and he would like to try and get him broken in. I feel a bit guilty really – we've had so little time and then of course we don't have a cart small enough to drive him in.'

'Well he looks to be the perfect build for driving,' Brenda admitted. 'But couldn't you make a start by breaking him to ride? That would get him used to traffic and work; then he'd be fittened up ready to break in to drive.'

'Broken to ride? Who could I get who would be small enough to do that?'

'I wish I could offer,' said Brenda, glancing ruefully at her callipers. 'But couldn't you ask . . . uno?'

'Of course!' I grinned.

So, in a matter of weeks, Bobby finally embarked on a useful life. After a round or two of enormously amusing pony-rodeo-tactics, during which he deposited Sharon on the ground a few times, only to have her climb grinning and undaunted straight back on board, he submitted gracefully. Once backed he was out and about for little rides showing great promise and a very sensible nature on the roads. George's pleasure the day that his smart little varnished trap and set of brown harness were delivered was only exceeded by his joy when, after a few weeks of driven work, he was able to take to the driver's seat, pick up his reins and finally set off at a sedate rumble for a 'bit of a drive out'.

Watching him go I was quite choked with emotion. I knew only too well how much freedom a set of horses' legs and two wheels can give when horizons and achievements have been cut back by disability. I'd experienced it myself and now I was seeing it happen for George.

How many other people must there be, how many, many people – even within reach of our corner of County Durham – who would benefit from the joy and the freedom that George was experiencing now? Watching him carefully turn the corner at the bottom of the back street before trotting out of view, I realized that there was a new tingle in the back of my mind. A tingle that harangued and harassed my conscience. A conscience that was reminding me that four years before, when driving Blizzard had been my one sanity-saving achievement in the awful months I was confined to a wheelchair and crutches, I had made a solemn promise: a promise that one day if ever I had the means to do it, I would try to bring that same freedom to other disabled people.

What the tingle was telling me was that that time was coming.

We really were well on the way to being able to start a Disabled Group, Brenda enthused. After all, we now had two ponies who were eminently suitable, a base for them to live at and loads of enthusiasm. Yes, all we were short of, I pointed out more cautiously, were disabled people who wanted to drive and vehicles for them to drive in – little things like that.

I must state at this point I never have and never will consider Brenda as 'disabled'. I am aware occasionally that she is 'hampered' by her metal-braced legs, but anyone with her determination and vitality – ably running a home, a car, a part-time job and a family – could never be described as 'disabled'. We soon came up with an interesting range of nicknames for Brenda. In a carriage she was 'Boadicea'; on the ground, irreverently, she was 'Clanky'; behind the wheel of her specially adapted car – well, Richard's usual phrase was simply 'Terrifying!'

It was, once again, Stella Hancock that came to the rescue. She was really the 'Grand Dame' of Disabled Driving, having devoted enormous amounts of her time and energy into getting groups founded since the sport's inception in 1977. A few phone calls to her, and a redundant vehicle especially adapted to take wheelchairs had been located and placed at our disposal. All we needed was to get it transported from down south to County Durham and it was ours.

No problem stated Brenda, and a week after clanking determinedly into the offices of a large local transport company, our 'Jubilee Cart' was collected and delivered. Free. It was called a 'Jubilee Cart' because this model, designed to be pulled by a pony and also to allow a wheelchair to be loaded on to it, originated in the year of the Queen's Silver Jubilee. I actually thought, on first laying eyes on it, that it resembled nothing more than a large black box on bicycle wheels. At no stretch of the imagination could it be described as 'elegant', but it was very functional, the back folding down to form a ramp up which the wheelchair could be pushed into place and a little seat alongside for the assistant driver.

Within a week both Bobby and Glint were bobbing merrily along in front of the awkward square contraption. Brenda and George were ecstatic: we now had the basic equipment to apply to start a Group.

Hadn't we overlooked a little something, I queried? Like members?

Although aware that there must be a large disabled population in County Durham just longing to get their hands on a pony and trap, trying to find one was not so simple. And for our first member we wanted someone who'd really benefit from the sport, someone with a sense of adventure and fun and a genuine liking of horses. Someone with enough enthusiasm to share it with those around them. In short, someone rather special. We exceeded even these exacting specifications when we found Heather Stoddart, someone very special indeed.

A phone call to a friend who had connections with Hexham Spinal Unit had produced her name. Well, it had seemed the obvious place to find people who were confined to wheelchairs. Heather was thirty, married and with twin sons aged nine. Active, sporty and full of fun, she had merely popped across to the local shop one day to buy a newspaper and a bar of chocolate. Re-crossing the road she was hit by a car and her neck was broken. That had been three years before and she was now permanently tetraplegic and faced with living the rest of her life in a wheelchair.

Before meeting her I was consumed with panic and guilt. Her story made me feel so inadequate and so very, very grateful at how lightly I had got off. My own accident had been paltry really; an insignificance next to Heather's. My six weeks' confinement in traction, which I had found nearly impossible to bear at times, had been but a blinking of an eye. My year of frustration with my crutches and wheelchair had been but a minor irritation. How on earth would I *feel* on meeting a person as disabled as Heather? Would I extend sympathy rather than empathy? Would she perceive me as a patronizing do-gooder?

On my first visit, after a nervous few minutes and a good cup of tea, I was to find it was Heather, the person, that held my attention and my admiration. Her disability and her wheelchair were mere incidentals. Although her 'hindrances' and 'obstacles' were much larger, Heather herself was no more 'disabled' than Brenda. Disability, I was rapidly discovering, was more to do with an attitude to life and a state of mind than a state of physical being.

6

Heather

In May 1987 the Montan Carriage Driving Team was on the road again, but this time the long road to Brighton didn't hold its usual horrors for us. I could hardly believe the luxury of being in a warm, comfortable cab, not having to crawl in first gear up every hill, of being able to carry out a conversation with Richard above the din of the engine. I felt opulent and arrogant as we purred past the spot where, the previous year, Plod had blown a core plug. We were making such good time I really couldn't believe how quickly we passed the scene of our second demise – the boiling battery.

Oh yes, this definitely was the life.

Seeing a large lay-by, Richard pulled in and switched off the engine. A quick feed and water for the horses and humans alike was called for and I leapt out on to the verge to stretch my legs, glad to be back on the road again. Excited at the prospect of the coming season: longing to hear for the first time 'next competitor, Richard Smith, current National Champion'.

'Come on,' said Richard, dripping the last few drops of tea on to the grass from his cup. 'Get yourselves back into the wagon girls, there's still a long way to go even at this speed!' Heather and Sharon climbed into the back and I got into the cab with Richard.

'All set?'

'You bet!'

'Let's go!'

The silence that ensued when Richard turned the key in the ignition was one of amazement, then embarrassment. Several times he turned the key and on each occasion there was a click – then nothing.

Stretched out on the grassy bankside, nose deep in the novel I had long since learned to carry as a precautionary measure, I awaited the arrival of the breakdown truck to fix the starter motor. I reflected that one of Great-aunt Meg's favourite maxims had been 'pride cometh before a fall'.

And far off, in that great scrapyard in the sky, I was uncomfortably aware that Plod was laughing her big-end off at us.

Brighton lived up to its usual springtime lushness and we were doing very well until the last two hazards in the marathon when the rubber tyre came off the back wheel and wrapped itself round and round the back axle and brakes, jamming the whole back end solid. Having to drag the whole contraption, like an over-weight sledge, slowed down the times drastically in those last two hazards and the run for the finish line, but straining and heaving with every last ounce of their strength, the Boys made the end of the course. After a cone round in which we redeemed ourselves for the previous year's cricket score, we finished in a respectable fourth place. But we were very aware that in these, the selection events for the World Championships in Germany, we needed to be doing even better.

If the weather at Brighton could be described as benign and spring-like that year, at Royal Windsor it could only be described as – wet. It poured for most of the four days, turning arena and stable area alike into a quagmire. Our roof in the trailer – as was its norm in moments of great stress – leaked and rain dripped in forlornly. Small rivers splashed off the edge of the horses' temporary stabling and flowed into their beds to make them damp and uncomfortable. But we did a super dressage test, a damn good marathon and a clear in the cones, to finish – to our great pride – in third place in this major international competition. On the final night the big question on everyone's mind as the horses lined up for the presentation ceremony was 'Will she? In all this rain and all this mud, could it be possible?'

But at exactly the appointed moment in the programme, the front of the Royal Box opened and a small figure in a brown tweed suit and sensible brown leather boots set off determinedly towards the waiting horses. She was followed closely by a taller lady, also in boots, carrying a large golfing umbrella over her head.

I really wasn't aware of the rain sluicing off my hat and down my collar, or of how tired I was after four days of hard work and tension. I was only aware that a few feet away from me Her Majesty the Queen, having signalled for Princess Anne to stay where she was, presumably for fear of frightening the horses with the umbrella, was now standing there in the deluge smiling and chatting to Richard as she handed him his rosette.

It was a gloriously proud moment for Richard and for Alan Robson, who had accompanied him in the carriage. I said a silent and fervent 'thank you' for having made the top three at Royal Windsor at last and prayed that it would set a seal on the rest of the season's results.

We were down to earth and back at home, and had time to regroup and recharge before the next crucial group of events – events which would decide the British Team for the World Championships in Germany. There were problems that needed sorting out and not a great deal of time to do so. Firstly and most obviously, we were short of a horse; a third horse without which we couldn't really hope for selection. In 1985 we had been very fortunate in being given the loan of a third horse from the Hancocks. The rules of International competition required a 'pair' to actually consist of three horses, so as to have a spare in case of injury. You could actually use your third horse for any section of the competition, which could be a tremendous advantage as you might have a horse that was brilliant on the marathon but not a dressage star. Before our sponsorship by Montan there was simply no way we could afford the upkeep of three horses, but now it was possible. I felt strongly that this time we needed to have a third horse that wasn't just ornamental but was a vital, working component of the team.

I was taken to see the proposed new horse, although I suspected my presence was purely a token one. 'Heather' belonged to a long-standing member of the driving fraternity called Donald Waite who lived in Lancashire. He'd owned this mare, who was thirteen years old, for over ten years. That pleased me as I like people who stick with their horses through thick and thin.

She had been bred as an eventer, out of an Irish Cob mare by a blood horse. 'Not so good', thought the Welsh Cob purist in me. However, Heather had not proved elegant enough as a dressage horse and so Donald had purchased her to drive in a pair. His daughter Amanda, however, recognizing the potential of her breeding, had grabbed her as a hunter and cross-country jumping horse and she had proved outstanding. In many ways Donald's daughter had had more success with Heather than her father.

Although she proved herself a superb marathon horse, tireless and powerful, Heather was never greatly talented in the dressage arena. More important, Donald had never found her 'better half'. He had made several attempts at finding another horse who would go as well as Heather, but without much success. In the end he got so disheartened that he had recently bought a couple of Hungarians that were already going on as a pair.

That was why, Richard rattled on enthusiastically, with Donald's daughter now away from home and Donald busy with his new purchases, Heather was really redundant. It had taken a great deal of persuasion on the phone, Richard continued, to get Donald to sell her because he and Amanda were still greatly attached to her and were half toying with the idea of a foal.

The plump and placid form dozing over the box door in the sun, her lower lip dangling as she snoozed, certainly wasn't quite what I'd expected.

'Aye, well of course the old lass has got a right belly on her at present,' apologized Donald. 'Always a good doer our Heather. By gum she likes her grub and she's done naught these last months really, just filled her belly. It'll come off her quicker than it's gone on. You'll get her as fit as fire in a crack!'

Heavy eyelids rose slowly to survey the cause of the disturbance to her afternoon nap.

'Come on lass,' said Donald, opening the door and taking hold of her head. 'Let's have you out here where we can see you proper like.'

With all the animation of an elderly milk-float horse, Heather ambled out on to the yard. Had she been a lady the phrases 'well made', 'handsome', and less politely, 'matronly' sprang to mind. She had a roman nose, the longest ears I'd seen not on a donkey and deep brown eyes that were pools of warm friendliness. She stood there motionless and untethered while Donald bustled off for a saddle and bridle.

'Oh she'll not go nowhere, not Heather,' he said as he

plonked a saddle on her back. 'Stand there all day – well, till she got hungry anyhow.'

Heather obligingly opened her mouth for a bit to be inserted and then closed her eyes again hoping to finish her siesta in peace.

'Right then, up you get!'

I realized that all eyes were turned on me and gulped. After several serious consequences, it is my golden rule *never* to ride an unknown quantity.

'Well I . . .'

'Oh just take her up that little hill there and back down towards us so we can see her action a bit. Don't fret yourself – she'll not do naught, not our Heather.'

As, slightly nervously, I hitched myself into the saddle, I soon feared this might prove to be only too true. Heels sinking into her ample flanks and belly, I kicked tentatively – with absolutely no response.

'Get on ye idle old thing!' shouted Donald giving her a hefty thwack on the rump.

With a reluctant grunt, Heather set away at a lollop up the hill. It really wasn't a trot, it was a lollop – nose stuck in the air, wheezing and grunting, she lolloped up the hill.

After the few hundred yards to the top she ran out of momentum anyway. She was as comfortable as an arm-chair – a delight to sit on in comparison to the high-actioned, bone-jarring trot of the Boys. On the return trip down the hill, gravity definitely contributed to acceleration and when we arrived back in the yard, I'd actually estab-lished contact with her mouth. For a mare that hadn't been ridden in months she was obviously bomb-proof. She was a sweetheart; a middle-aged lady with a weight problem. But was she, I wondered, the powerhouse we so badly needed? Did she have the courage, the stamina, the 'fire in the belly' that Richard had come to rely on in our Welsh Cobs?

Her blood line showed in her ultra-fine velvety coat, the

neat little feet and slim ankles, the blood vessels that showed just beneath the surface after even our short exertion. Her more doughty Irish ancestry showed in her overall build and massive muscular chest, her huge frame. I commented on her incredibly powerful hindquarters, no doubt developed in her cross-country jumping career.

'Oh Aye, got a grand arse on her,' confirmed Donald. 'Let me tell you something about this mare,' he said, looking me straight in the eye. 'They all scoffed at our Amanda when she took Heather to some fancy one-day Event thing, "Here comes Amanda Waite riding her father's cart horse" they announced to the crowd, oh aye, I know what they all think when they look at our Heather – I know what you're thinking now an' all – but they laughed on t'other side of their faces when she won the cup that day, against all of them skinny-legged thoroughbred creatures with long fancy names. We've no need to sell the mare: she owes me and this family naught after all she's done, she'd be quite happy just grazing her head off for the rest of her days, and she'd be a grand mother an' all. But I'd like to see her back at what she's good at.

'I know your horses are good and that's what this lass has never had – a good partner.'

Still untethered, the object of this discussion had quietly dozed off once more where she stood. 'That's why I've decided you can have her, if you want – to see if you can give her what I never did: a chance to show them all just how bloody good she really is!'

Was it possible, just remotely possible, that beneath that placid exterior beat the heart of a lion? Burnt the fires of determination? Lay the strength of a bull? Well, until we got her home, got two hundredweight of belly off her and hours of muscle fittening work into her, we couldn't really tell. But one thing I did know: I liked this chestnut lady with the long ears and the soft silky coat. I liked her very much indeed and I suspected that somehow her appearance was going to prove very, very deceptive.

As we shook hands on the deal, made arrangements to return with the box in a few days' time and prepared to leave, I just caught the lid of her supposedly sleeping eye flicker up and then down at me. Just once.

Was she winking? What surprises did this foxy-red lady have up her fetlock? What paths, adventures and trials were we destined to share together?

Suddenly I wanted her home as quickly as possible, wanted her into work and into the rapidly growing team of people and horses that made up my life. What I could never have guessed was how quickly and how deeply she was going to settle herself into our hearts and our lives.

Surveying our new horse and our head groom in close proximity for the first time, I realized they had more in common than a name: there was a remarkable likeness in frizzy ginger hair and rather ample hindquarters. However, for Heather – the mare that is – these attributes were about to undergo a rapid transformation.

Out came the clippers and off came her mane. Because the Boys were hogged it was important that, physically, she matched them as closely as possible. Next, I did what I could with her tail. Compared with the Boys' thick glossy waterfalls of hair, Heather's tail was a pathetic trickle. It looked as if it had been chewed by the cows all summer, coupled with a fair demolition job scrubbing the top out against a fence post. Nevertheless, a good shampoo, an untangle and neat trim to bang it level with her hocks did improve it one hundred per cent. The waistline, I realized, was going to take a little longer.

Work began straight away – two walk rides a day, stepped up after a week to three. Grazing was limited to the 'starvation' paddock, where we kept the ponies so they didn't gorge themselves to laminitis, and her hay was strictly rationed. After a few days we carefully began a little hard feed in her diet, stepping it up as her work increased.

Heather quickly earned my admiration for the manner in which she took to these privations: many horses who are 'good doers' take less than kindly to a substantial reduction in rations, turning snappy and bad tempered. Come to think of it, I know a few people like that too!

But Heather just sighed a lot and ate the tiny meals that were offered to her with gratitude rather than contempt.

The Boys accepted her arrival with little or no fuss. At first.

I was aware that Bear had been following Heather solicitously around the field. I hadn't failed to notice the little nicker of welcome that he now trilled out whenever Heather returned to the yard after yet another ride out. But one day, as the Boys grazed peacefully in the big field and Heather stood stoically in her paddock, I witnessed something quite amazing. Bear suddenly lifted his head from the grass for no apparent reason, set off at a determined walk, right across the field towards the paddock, stretched his neck across the dividing wire and gave Heather a very affectionate nuzzle on the neck and then resumed grazing quietly near by.

I nearly fell off the gate as realization hit me: Bear was in love. After fifteen years, he had, it appeared, met the woman of his dreams. Had he perceived behind her plain, placid face and in her ample frame, qualities of which we were as yet unaware? Was he indicating to us that here was a lady he could do business with – in the nicest possible way of course?

True to Donald's word, the flesh was almost melting off Heather and she was hardening up and getting fitter every day. Soon the time came when a slightly miffed Blizzard gazed over his stable door as Heather was brought out (in *his* harness!) and placed alongside Bear and traces attached to the carriage. After a bit of eye boggling at the unfamiliar vehicle and the unfamiliar work partner, both horses set off fidgeting down the back street and then swung on to the road and set away at a spanking trot. By the time they returned to the yard it was if they had driven together all their lives. United in rhythm and response, they drew up into the yard as one. Richard was jubilant.

'Power!' he cried as he jumped off the cart. 'At last I've got the power – and my God she's not even fit yet! What a mare! What a pair!' he crooned and kissed and slapped their necks and stuffed handfuls of Polos into their mouths. Then we all became aware of a rather sad and dejected little face hanging over a loosebox door. Filled with guilt, Richard hurried over with a handful of mints.

'But she'll not do for dressage,' he reassured Blizzard, tugging his ears the way Blizzard liked best. 'The stride is too different and the head carriage wrong. No, I'll still be depending on you for the fancy footwork.' Somewhat cheered, Blizzard crunched his Polos.

It would appear that in theory we had achieved what we had set out to do: have three horses, two of which were an obvious dressage pair, two an obvious marathon pair and any two of which could do the obstacle driving. All we had to do now was prove it in practice – and quickly, if we were to achieve selection for the World Championships. An awful lot rested on Heather's ample shoulders.

7

The Inspection

As well as Heather's rapid induction into our ways and the constant hard work to get her fit and ready at such a late point in the season, hard work had already begun on a different front. With Bobby and Glint now driving regularly and well, and an enthusiastic core of people helping with the training, we felt ready to take the giant step of applying to become a member driving group of the Riding for the Disabled Association.

As with all good British institutions, the group's first requirement was a committee. We had in Brenda and myself an obvious Treasurer and Group Organizer but were stumped for a little while trying to find a secretary. The right person needed to be in command of clerical and administrative skills as well as having a working knowledge of horses and ponies, an interest in the disabled and some spare time to offer. Not an easily found combination of virtues.

One day at College I needed some advice on the dates of courses I'd been asked to teach and found myself directed to the registrar's office. I hadn't been in for thirty seconds before the registrar noticed the horse medallion around my neck. Within the first minute I'd told her about our Welsh Cobs and our driving, then she told me about the Welsh Cob she used to own. It took about ten minutes to discuss the embryonic driving group, and by the time I left – almost half an hour later and nearly late for my next lecture – I knew I'd found in Hazel Hindmarch a good friend, an ally and a committee secretary.

Finally, after years of wishing and months of hard work the date was set: the Inspectors were coming. The rules laid down by the RDA to govern Driving for the Disabled are strict, and safety is the paramount consideration. Before any disabled driver is allowed out under their banner, the ponies, vehicles and harness to be used have to be inspected and tested and must be passed as being satisfactory, as must the able-bodied helpers. For a whole week, every piece of two sets of harness were scrubbed and rubbed and polished till they shone and two ponies were scrubbed and rubbed and polished likewise. Our pride and joy, our Jubilee cart, was washed and polished and tyres were pumped up to the right pressure. Scones and cakes were baked, the best tea service was dug out and, finally, we were as ready as it was humanly possible to be.

The three ladies from the RDA were very charming. Middle-aged and gracefully 'County', they did a thorough and unhurried inspection of everything: first I drove Bobby and then they drove Bobby. First Brenda drove Glint, and then they drove Glint. Finally, and only when every last buckle of harness had been inspected and the ponies pronounced suitable, Heather Stoddart had her big moment. The ramp came down on the back of the Jubilee cart and up she went. When her wheelchair was locked safely in position, I was able at long last to give her her first real taste of driving. Somewhat miffed at having to go out for a third time, Bobby nevertheless obligingly trotted down the lane. Heather of course could not yet drive the pony, but for that first trip she was content to sit and watch and listen and enjoy the fresh air brushing past her face. Whatever hard work and organizational problems we had

had in the previous months, it was all worth it just for the pleasure Heather received on that first drive.

Inspection successfully over, we retired to the house for a slap-up home-baked tea, to celebrate our acceptance as a provisional group.

The ladies from the RDA were well into their second cup of Earl Grey and the seedy cake when there were three heavy knocks at the front door. A sense of foreboding came over me as I opened the door to find a neat little man in a grey suit.

'Mrs Smith?'

'. . . umm . . . Yes?'

'Wife of Richard Smith?'

'Yes . . .'

'Former proprietor of a second-hand furniture shop in Bishop Auckland?'

'Yes?'

'I'm from the Sheriff's office. You've been issued with a Court Summons regarding outstanding rates on the shop you vacated. This has been ignored. As a result I am empowered to remove property up to the value of . . .'

My God! It was a bailiff! I'd never even *seen* a letter about the rates. When had that come? Was it buried somewhere in the heap of papers on Richard's desk? Oh Lord!

Behind me, the dear ladies politely sipped their tea from my best china and nibbled at the seedy cake, looking in mild interest at the newcomer at the door before continuing their chatter with Heather in her wheelchair. I turned round to Brenda – my face registering complete panic – and mouthed silently *'Bay-liff!'*

Brenda, I must add, is no stranger to financial straits; she's the sort of friend who wouldn't be shocked by someone coming to cart off the furniture in the middle of a tea party. But the dear ladies . . . what would they think? What sort of decadent person was I? Certainly not the sort to run a disabled group!

Brenda was magnificent. She strategically placed all four foot ten of her might between the scenario at the front door and the ladies at the tea table and began a diversionary tactic.

I must admit, Mr Bailiff was a polite and patient man. He stood on the doorstep quite motionless, clipboard in hand. I had the feeling he would stay there all night if necessary.

'May I come in Mrs Smith?'

'Well, umm, actually it's terribly inconvenient at the moment. I don't suppose there's any chance of you coming back in say, an hour?' My straw-clutching was met with a slow, solemn shake of the head. 'No?' Why was Richard *never* there when crises struck? He'd fled, of course, at the prospect of a tea party. 'Look, how much exactly is this rate thing?'

'With the Court costs now incurred, exactly £198.00. Of course, Mrs Smith, if you can pay me the requisite sum then there'd be no need for me to enter the property and seize goods.'

Seize goods! Seize goods? Dear God, I didn't have a great deal of material splendour around me, but what I did have was either much loved or essential. Seize goods indeed! I tilted slightly on to the offensive. 'Look, of course I haven't got £198.00. I wouldn't be so stupid as to keep that sort of money in the house. I doubt I've got a fiver. I honestly can't remember us getting a rate demand for the shop, but I'm not disputing that you're right. Can I give you a cheque instead?' Even as I said it I felt sick – I knew there wasn't £198.00 in the account.

'Sorry, Mrs Smith, I've no guarantee a cheque won't bounce.'

Brenda was doing her best to keep the conversation going, but she was obviously flagging.

'I can give you a cheque for £50.00, guaranteed with a cheque card. That won't bounce. You can't refuse the offer to pay off some of the debt – I'm sure I've read that somewhere before!'

'Well, I . . .'

'Look, please! I can give you £50.00 now and I'll sign something, *anything*, to say you'll have the rest in twenty-eight days.' Another month of bread and water loomed ahead, but I did feel a glimmer of hope that my home wasn't going to be dismantled. '*Please!*'

Perhaps he took pity on me. Perhaps he thought that with two disabled people in the house I deserved a little leniency. Perhaps he just thought I was stone mad.

'I'll go and get my bag.' I flew to the kitchen.

When I returned it was to find, to my horror, that he was in the dining room, eyeing-up the stereo, writing things on his clipboard. The ladies looked mildly astonished – even Brenda looked as though it was a lost cause. I rushed in and grabbed him by the elbow. 'Excuse me,' I gushed to the ladies. 'Insurance man, you know. Valuations due and all that – must pay this gentleman the premium. So sorry, do please finish your tea, I'll not be a minute.'

With a fixed grin on my face I propelled him into the kitchen and shut the door. 'What are you *doing*?' I hissed hysterically.

'Well, Mrs Smith, I do have to write down the value of property that would cover the remainder of the debt if you fail to honour the agreement in twenty-eight days.'

I scribbled out the cheque as hastily as I could, but not in time to stop him peering into the fridge-freezer and eyeing-up the microwave.

'How old is this, Mrs Smith?'

I pushed the cheque into his hands and signed the form on his clipboard, pledging not my soul in default but my microwave. 'There's fifty pounds, guaranteed. Now look, please, Mr . . . whoever . . . I'm in the middle of a most important meeting. I don't wish to rush you but . . .'

'Oh, I'm so sorry, Mrs Smith, if I've caused any inconvenience.'

My smile was watery – my lovely day ruined, my success in ashes. 'I'm sure you're just doing your job; how nice it must be to have one,' I said as I propelled him out of the back door so as not to run the gauntlet of the tea party again.

Knees knocking and hands shaking I refilled the kettle and sank down at the kitchen table. Why today? Why on earth today? And then slowly, as so often happens, the funny side crept through. I bet not a single one of those dear ladies even knew what a bailiff was – let alone had come face to face with one. It could have been both educational and entertaining.

I'd played my hand all wrong. I should have taken him in and introduced him. 'Now ladies; this gentleman is from the Sheriff's office. No, they don't only have them in Westerns. So ladies, this is the bailiff: Mr Bailiff these are the ladies of the Riding for the Disabled Committee. Now, the bailiff would like to remove a few things because I can't pay my bills. Shall we start with you, Mrs Roberts? What do you think that chair you're sitting on is worth – thirty pounds? Forty? What do *you* think Mr Bailiff? Could you get up, Mrs Roberts, so he can have a better look? So kind. Thirty-five? Fair enough. Now, Heather, if you'd just move your wheelchair so he can get a better look at that side table . . .'

I made a fresh pot and, grinning at Brenda, rejoined the party.

'More tea, ladies?'

8

The Real Thing

Heather more than fulfilled every hope and dream we had laid at her stable door: all the potential Donald Waite had prophesied had been proven in her partnership with Bear. Together they proved to be a tireless, incredibly manoeuvrable pair of horses, whose consistency of performance on marathons earned us our longed-for place on the British team. Initial elation was replaced by much hard work and preparation and then the worrying realization that this time we were competing on foreign soil, around continental courses and against pairs from countries who, in the two years since the first World Championships, had taken their sport from the 'amateur' to a very high professional level.

I was soon to wonder whether Heather had done us all – including herself – a favour or a disservice. The journey from Stanley Crook to Germany was in itself a challenge and ordeal of stamina and endurance. It was fifty-eight hours after we had left home that our horsebox and trailer, containing three cobs, ourselves and Sharon and Heather, crawled into the British Army base at Paderborn where we were to rest for four days. Apart from one overnight stay at the shipping stable at Dover, the horses had been in the box for the whole of the journey. My heart had been torn for them but there had been no option and Bear, Blizzard and Heather earned my undying admiration for their stoic acceptance of their long and uncomfortable confinement. It was little consolation that their human companions were more exhausted than they were. Finally, after four days' 'rest and recuperation' – and marvellous hospitality from the British Army – we completed the last leg of the journey to Reisenbeck.

Reisenbeck was actually a large country estate with its own 'schloss' and Baron and had been developed as a high standard equestrian and show centre with its own leisure and holiday facilities, including a large Alpine style hotel in the grounds. All this I could see in the distance – the flags, the hotel, the large grandstand – as the box rumbled round the very last corner of its 750-mile journey. I was a little dismayed, therefore, when signs and efficient German hands directed us away from the mirage beyond the trees and towards a huge, barren, newly harvested stubble field. A vast area of the field had been encircled with high, heavy mesh fencing surmounted with barbed wire and, at the one and only entrance gate, at least four security guards scrutinized the papers of every slowly entering vehicle, whilst another two patrolled up and down with dogs that gave a new dimension to the word 'Alsatian'.

I was just about to make a merry quip to Richard about looking out for the watch towers and machine guns when my eyes lit upon an unmistakable shape. Oh it was fairly carefully concealed but, camouflage netting or not, it was nevertheless a large tank! With an equally large gun barrel! Could this 'World Championship' bit all be some sort of elaborate hoax I wondered? Surely they wouldn't have lured us and all our horses all this way just to hold us hostage or something? Jokes I had made about Colditz earlier in the day were suddenly less funny.

We were allocated stables which turned out to be small

wooden compartments with not very high sides inside a huge, stifling marquee. I was not at all happy as the place was like a sauna and the boxes so small that I feared the cobs might go down for a roll and get 'cast' in them. The menace of cross-infection from all those closely confined horses also worried me. We voiced our fears to our Chef d'Equipe, and pointed out that we had our own portable stabling with us which the cobs were well used to. I felt much happier once three familiar chestnut bums were poking out from the side of our horsebox, where they belonged.

The United States Equestrian Team (USET) were not hard to locate. As at Sandringham, an entire row of boxes had been commandeered by them and the whole row decorated and emblazoned with red, white and blue awnings, bunting and stars and stripes. The horses, equally resplendent in red, white and blue rugs, all looked over doors that had beautifully hand-painted signs proclaiming their name, age and parentage. Every third box or so did not contain a horse, but had been rigged out as a temporary harness, tack and feed room and every piece of equipment gleamed with mirror-finish blue paint and the USET emblem. A swarming army of young men and women in red, white and blue sweatshirts beavered away with red, white and blue shovels, brushes and grooming kit. At least, I thought, the horses aren't red, white and blue!

I knew that all of this equipment, all these people would have been provided by the USET who gave equal backing to *any* equestrian discipline that took place outside of the USA. So, be it three-day eventing at the Olympics, or carriage driving in Germany, the same organization and support – in finance as well as equipment and personnel -- would be there behind the American competitors.

I travelled along the stable lines suitably awed by it all. It was not a person I recognized first, it was a horse. Well, as the only Appaloosas I knew of in the pair driving world,

Charlie Cheston's spotted horses were pretty easily identified. A young man was engaged in carefully rubbing the horse along its backbone, but paused in his work to say 'Hi' and to chat.

'Are you a member of Mr Cheston's crew?' I asked. 'A groom or shotgun?'

'Oh no,' he replied pleasantly. 'I don't belong to any one particular driver. I'm here for the whole American team. I'm the official osteopath and masseur for the horses. I work alongside our vet and trainer – though I've been known to give the odd aching driver a rub down too!'

'Oh!' was all I could manage to say. The official vet, the official masseur, official trainers. Hotel suites and chartered planes. I thought about Sharon and Heather who had sole responsibility for the day-to-day welfare of our horses. Our little 'pit ponies' from County Durham. My spirits sank ever lower. It was not jealousy or envy – it was a sense of utter inadequacy. 'Well, tell Mr Cheston that Carol Smith was asking for him and I'll catch up with him before long.'

'Sure will! So long!' and his experienced hands continued their quest for little knots of tension. How I wished they could have wrought their magic on my spirit.

The next morning we awoke to find ourselves surrounded by a sea of red mud. It had rained in solid sheets all night and the constant passage of vehicles had simply liquidized the red, sandy field. Through that red sea in the early afternoon, a procession of fifty of the world's best pairs of horses slithered and squelched and splattered. Carriage wheels that had taken hours to polish and horses' legs that had taken even longer to clean were soon uniformly covered in the ghastly, sandy soup. At least, I thought ruefully as Bear and Blizzard picked their way with obvious distaste towards the collecting field, we were all in the same boat. But what a shame, what a waste of time and effort and pride.

The opening ceremony did a lot to raise spirits, despite the mud, and to make us feel that we'd actually come to the purpose of our visit – to play out the second World Pairs Driving Championships. As in the Olympic Games each country was led in alphabetical order into the arena by a flag bearer on a large German dressage horse. A maximum crowd of several thousand crowded the grandstand and an Oompah band let forth at full blast at one end – which caused some of the competitors to come round that corner rather faster than they might have wished. When, finally, as the host nation, the German team, with Erkhart Meineker in the forefront, drove into the arena, a roar went up that wouldn't have disgraced a Cup Final at Wembley. This man I realized was a *hero* in his country, a sportsman with nationwide recognition.

How little they seemed, our British Welsh Cobs. How short in the leg and the back compared with the tall, long legged and necked thoroughbreds that comprised the vast majority of the continental entries. We were, I realized, somewhat awed by the size and spectacle of it all, really only amateurs when pitted against major contenders in that arena – the Germans, the Hungarians, the Polish, the Swiss and the Americans. What tack could we possibly take at this late stage to improve our chances? What on *earth* could we possibly do? What we always did was the answer that lay in my heart. Our very best.

By the end of the dressage day I think we all realized our very best wasn't going to be nearly good enough. Everything we had been forewarned about in the build up to the event had proved to be prophetically true: whatever the British were doing with their horses in that dressage arena, it wasn't what the continentals were wanting to see.

Though not last, the British Team, including Christine Dick who had perhaps been our greatest hope, were well down the final pecking order.

That afternoon, after even more rain, the marathon course and hazards were announced open for inspection. Some of the elements were, in my mind anyway, potentially lethal to the horses and would not, I was sure, have been allowed at home. Walking the course with Richard, I tried to imagine what damage such hazards could cause to horses who got straddled across the top of them. By the following day I was to find out.

I don't think I had ever felt so nervous on a marathon day. I could only send Bear and Heather off into the unknown with my prayers for a safe return whispered into their necks, and after that could only range around the show field unsettled and anxious. I had to drag myself by sheer willpower to sit behind the final hazard – the only place on the course I could bear to actually *see* the cobs because I knew that if they got that far then they must surely make it home.

The first shock came when the public address system – relaying messages efficiently in three languages – announced that John Roger, first British Team member to face the marathon, had had to retire with a broken axle. That meant the team score now rested on Richard and Christine's shoulders and the thought did not hearten me. Every time Richard finished a section of the marathon and his name and number were given out, my heart pounded and my head swam.

Section by section he completed the course until only the final section remained. The hazards.

'Richard Smith, Great Britain, safely through Hazard One.'

'Richard Smith, Great Britain, safely through Hazard Two.' Standing up was out of the question: my legs were pure jelly, my knee joints disengaged. I knelt on the grass by the railings around the last hazard and prayed the minutes away, longing for each hazard to be over, gazing at the horizon until my eyes ached for those two familiar, beloved chestnut shapes to appear.

'Richard Smith, Great Britain. Unfortunate problem in Hazard Three. Richard Smith, Great Britain, retires Hazard Three.' On legs that moments before had been jelly, I ran and ran until my chest heaved and my lungs felt they must burst. Richard Smith 'retires'? Richard wouldn't do that lightly, not here, not on such a day. For him to have given up there must be something very wrong with either the horses or the vehicle. And if it were the vehicle, surely they would have announced it as they had done with John Roger? So it had to be the horses – but which? Or both? And what was wrong?

I raced back to our horsebox and my heart only began to beat normally again when, a few moments later, two utterly dejected figures trudged through the camp gates leading two equally dejected horses, their traces flapping forlornly against their hindquarters.

James Robson, our sponsor's son, had accompanied Richard on the marathon as shotgun. He was leading Bear and my first assessment was that he seemed all right – walking evenly, but very, very slowly. Behind him came Richard leading Heather and as I ran towards them I saw why Bear and James were walking so slowly. They did not want to leave Heather and Richard behind.

Heather's tail was matted with blood, and dark crimson streams trickled down her hind legs. She walked so stiffly and slowly that it was as if each step was a determined, pre-judged agony, an evil necessity to get her home.

'Oh my God!' I whispered. 'What happened?'

'The logs,' Richard almost whispered back, the moisture bright in his eyes. 'She slipped back on the hazard with the logs and got impaled on one of those uprights. Come on my bonny lass, come on just a little further.'

Grunting with the effort and discomfort, Heather waddled forward, her big plain features set in a grimace. I steeled myself to look closer at her injuries. She appeared to have developed an udder, a huge round pendulous swelling just where a cow's udder would be, but in front of her own small, virginal teats. That look was sufficient. Could she have pierced her abdominal wall? Was this a massive rupture?

'Get her back carefully,' I shouted over my shoulder as I headed off at a run again. 'I'm going for the vet!'

On my way to the stable manager I passed Sharon and Heather, both pale and obviously shaken. I answered their unasked question for them.

'It's Heather. She's hurt, but we're not sure how badly. I'm going for the vet. Get back as quick as you can – boil water, get the First Aid kit out. Hurry!'

The girls sped off in their direction as quickly as I went in mine.

At the entrance gate the stable manager quickly put out a call for the vet and equally quickly a Mercedes four-wheel drive vehicle sped into the compound bringing in two polite young German men who spoke excellent English. By now Heather was really sore and cross and in no mood to be prodded and poked. She flattened her ears and glowered and jumped with great grunts of pain whenever they tried to examine her.

'Twitch?' I suggested desperately as I hung on to her lead rope for grim death. Apparently that term is quite recognizable to German vets and, nodding in agreement, they produced a long and very professional implement from their vehicle.

Remembering the relief it had brought little Bobby when he was in such pain, I had no qualms whatsoever and thankfully slipped the rope loop over the flexible end of Heather's nose, twisting it tightly. Gradually she became less tense, less agitated. She wasn't actually relaxed, and

he elegant Alastair prepares for dressage at Holker Hall, 1986.

Two red-headed Heathers entered our lives in 1987 – Heather Baldwin is on the right!

Two of the many girl groom trainees who worked and lived alongside the horses: Lisa and Jo with Bear, 1987.

In 1987 the Wear Valley Carriage Driving for the Disabled group was founded: Heather Stoddart *(right)* driving our original Jubilee Cart.

By late 1987 Brenda Harrison *(left)* was winning cups and rosettes with her pony Glint. *(Hazel Hindmarch)*

By 1989 the group boasted this superb Ruskin Rambler, proudly driven here by Heather Stoddart and myself at Nostell Priory. *(Colin Stoddart)*

With Heather on the team in 1987, Richard drove to an indisputable National Championship victory. Here Heather and Bear power through the hazards at Sandringham.

1988 began in glorious form: here, at Islabank, Bear and Blizzard do a lap of honour after winning the event. *(Anne Grossick)*

Disaster in 1988. One minute Blizzard and Heather are powering through the water hazard . . . the next, everything comes to a shuddering halt in hazard six as Richard's leg is shattered. *(Anne Grossick)*

At Islabank in 1989 it seemed as though we were back on form. Richard had recovered and the team came in second overall. *(Anne Grossick)*

The middle of the 1989 season was disastrous. Here Heather narrowly misses serious injury as the vehicle snaps in two in the water hazard.

The ups and downs of the 1989 season vividly symbolized as Heather and Blizzard tackle the dreaded 'bridge' at the National Championships, Windsor. *(Hazel Hindmarch)*

Sweet success! At the National Championships, Windsor, 1989, Richard was to become Reserve Champion. *(Hazel Hindmarch)*

With Bear on his eighteenth birthday in 1990, proudly showing off his birthday rosette from Daphne Lane. *(Daphne Lane)*

A remarkable lady with her remarkable patient: Daphne 'Laser' Lane with Bear after his successful treatment in 1990. *(Donald Lane)*

The Strang Centre, 1994. Bear brings pleasure and achievement to one of my disabled students from Peterlee College.

she certainly wasn't happy, but at least she was prepared to stand still.

It was infuriating to be at Heather's nose when all the diagnosis was going on under her tummy. Then, just as I was beginning to fear the very worst, one of the vets reassured me. 'She is very, very cut and bruised under her belly and between her back legs. But it's all superficial – a lot of hair and chunks of skin missing but that's all.'

'Oh, thank God,' I breathed with relief. 'But what's that huge swelling? I thought she had ruptured herself or something – it's getting bigger all the time.'

'It's a haematoma – blood blister if you like – and, yes, it's a huge one, but it will have no long-term effect on her.'

'Mr Smith,' a vet politely addressed Richard. 'I would like now to give the mare some injections to ease her discomfort and also to help take away all this swelling. It's all I can really do because the cuts and lacerations you can, I'm sure, clean up yourself. However, you must realize that once she has had these injections, she will not pass a blood test: you could not use her again in competition for two weeks.'

'Give her whatever she needs,' Richard said. 'This mare will be doing no more work here I assure you and not for a long while to come.'

Heather accepted the needles like the stoic lady she was and, after the vets had gone promising to return on the morrow, we moved her gently into a knee-deep straw bed and I began to bathe her cuts as tenderly as I could. To this she submitted almost thankfully, though I guess the pain-killers were also taking effect.

Back at the marathon, though Gordon Henderson, the British Individual, survived, Christine Dick did not and we had to face the awful sight of the entire British team being wiped off the scoreboard.

Some slight solace could be taken from the fact that we were not alone in our defeat. A quarter of all the pairs of horses that set off on the marathon retired or were eliminated for one reason or another. It had indeed been a killer.

And so it was over. On the final evening we were treated to what was quite simply the most breathtaking display of the equestrian art that could ever have been devised. From all over Germany and beyond, every conceivable breed and type of horse demonstrated just about everything the known mind could devise for horses to do. But of all the sights in that Reisenbeck arena that night, though many made me gasp in admiration, only one brought tears to my eyes: a display by the German Welsh Cob Society. I realized then, finally perhaps, why our horses would never be accepted as cross-country or dressage horses in our hosts' eyes. The Welsh Cobs that trotted around the arena that night were all presented in a very fixed role – rustic horses, country horses, family-drive-around-the-lane horses. Every pair and single and tandem that appeared was pulling a varnished vehicle, a 'country' cart with drivers in tweeds and national costume. The horses all had their full feather and manes and coats on and were show-ring plump and truly 'cobby'.

In our livery and our smart carriage and our hogged manes, clean-shaven legs and banged tails, did we create some sort of dilemma for the continental mind by insisting on driving our Welsh Cobs the way we did? Had I been deceiving myself all these years imagining that within the Welsh Cobs I owned and used and loved burnt extraordinary fires of stamina and determination? That they were possessed of a special courage and presence that made me quite humble at times? Were we *wrong* in keeping them hard and sleek and competition fit? Were we abusing them by asking them to perform dressage tests and feats of endurance across country?

And then I saw him.

He was about four to six months old, bright chestnut with a flash of white on his forehead, his tail still a short wand of flaxen curls. He wore a little leather foal slip on his head and was attached from this by a leather rein to the shaft of the cart to which his mother was harnessed.

Into that huge arena, with its noisy crowd of thousands and under artificial floodlights and Oompah bands, trotted the mare and her son. And was he terrified? Did he panic at the strange noise and light and movement? Admittedly he did blink momentarily, but after that he *revelled* in it. As his mother stretched out her forelegs into the lovely and unique action of the Welsh Cob, he tucked in level and close beside her, arched his little neck and flicked his little fore-legs as if to say 'See! Look at me! I have it in me too!' The generations of versatility and strength and grace.

Bred by the thrifty Welsh farmer who wanted one horse to do three jobs – work his farm on a weekday, drive to Chapel on a Sunday and hunt like hell across country on a Wednesday – he indeed had it all: it was his heritage, though far removed in time and distance from the hills of Wales. And I sent a silent thank you to that cheeky, bold little chap, who had made me realize that as long as I valued my cobs for what they were and they enjoyed being what they were, then what we were doing with them could never be wrong.

We stood in the arena that last afternoon, nation beside nation in alphabetical order as we had been just a few short days before at the opening ceremony. The winners' podium was surrounded by flowers, medals were pre-sented, national anthems played and the crowds cheered. In those closing minutes, though I could have been for-given for feeling sad or even slightly bitter that no glory was ours, I began to feel strangely proud. Proud just to have been there at all. Proud to have had the opportunity at least to try.

We'd been defeated, it was true, but we had still achieved – all of us – what we had set out to do, to represent our country to the *best* of our ability. Surely no one could deny we had done that?

The bands struck up gently into *Auf Wiedersehen* and, like the spokes of a giant wheel, one by one the nations' pairs of horses lined up three abreast and we circled the arena to wave goodbye, to truly end the second World Championships.

By nightfall everything was dismantled, packed and loaded. Horsebox engines that had been idle for nearly a week grumbled into life and diesel fumes filled the air. There was little time to be sentimental about leaving or even to say goodbye to certain friends we didn't know if we would ever have the chance to see again.

Charles and Lois Cheston from the USA, with their lovely spotty horses and their bottomless First Aid kit, had fixed us up with all the supplies and drugs needed to ensure that Heather had a comfortable journey home. It was now a race to get across Germany and Belgium through the night to reach the ferry the following morning.

There was a certain poignancy as the endless line of wagons streamed out of gates now thrown wide open and unguarded, to scatter horses and people across the entire northern hemisphere. The mournful booming of air horns was the last farewell the World's drivers could give to Reisenbeck 1987 and the 'Weltmeisterchaft Der Zweispenner Fahrer.'

Our return home was not to peace, quiet and recuperation, it was straight into the last two events of the home driving calendar: Castle Howard and the National Championships at Windsor. It was perhaps lunacy to attempt Castle

Howard with horses so newly returned from a long journey. It was obviously out of the question to use Heather, and so Blizzard, who had spent the last month in a dressage role and was not truly fit, had to do all three sections. He was withdrawn by the vet at the halt because his respiration rate was not dropping rapidly enough.

There was now only one event left, one last chance to redeem and prove ourselves. The National Championships.

After the build up and excitement of the World Championships and the subsequent disappointment and exhaustion, it was very hard to motivate ourselves for another supreme effort. However, the fact remained that Richard was still the current National Champion and that title, gained in circumstances that in some sad way had devalued it all year, had to be defended.

Once she was returned to her routine at home Heather made a rapid and total recovery from all the bumps and abrasions she had suffered in Germany. The 1987 National Championships were held at their traditional base in Windsor Great Park, and we headed south with the combination of horses Richard had chosen for the World Championships; Bear and Blizzard for the dressage and Bear and Heather for the marathon. They had the power, the speed and stamina Richard knew he would need on that long and demanding course.

Their dressage test was a dream, the scores were virtually level with Christine Dick, and well ahead of the rest of the class. It was to be the familiar battle of the Titans. Though firm and old friends, there existed between Richard and Christine a deep awareness that on the day there would be no pulled punches, they would both be going all out to win the title. And this year, more than anything, Richard wanted a clear win, a conclusive win. We needed to come up with the real thing.

Waiting, heart in mouth, at the end of the marathon I could detect in Heather just a slight trailing in her right hind leg and her pace slackened momentarily. Then she leant harder into her collar as if gritting her teeth and saying 'Come on, pull yourself together, lass, not far now'. Beside her, Bear took up the momentary slack in her traces as if aware that his friend – his partner – needed him to call upon the very special reserves he possessed. The pace quickened again and with each hoofbeat they drew nearer until I could hear the rattle of the swingletrees and the rumble of the carriage wheels. Then in a blur they were past me, through the flags and drawing up at the halt.

When the scores went up an hour later we were in the lead! Truly and unequivocally in the lead. Richard even had a few points in hand for the cone competition the next day, which meant that he didn't have to get a clear round to win.

Nevertheless, win he did. Without time faults or a cone down, Bear and Blizzard completed the course the next day to make Richard the National Champion of 1987. Conclusively, unreservedly – the winners. This time it was the real thing.

All the strain, effort and exhaustion of the season that lay behind us now became completely worthwhile. The knockers and the mockers who had mumbled about our defeat in Germany and our elimination at Castle Howard would now surely be silenced – for a little while anyway. It was a gratifying and splendid end to a somewhat frustrating year. The horses had come up trumps at the end and I was a very contented lady. I didn't think anything could give me more pleasure or pride than to have the magnificent bronze Famous Grouse trophy roosting on our dining table for yet another year.

I was to be proved wrong. For the year was not yet quite over.

9

Red Flags

When motor cars were first allowed along our country roads, they were considered so very revolutionary, alarming and dangerous that a man with a red flag was required to proceed in front to warn all persons of the contraption's approach, thus, inevitably, restricting the car to a walking speed.

In many ways a similar attitude prevailed over carriage driving for the disabled. It was indeed a potentially alarming and dangerous prospect to have a perhaps seriously handicapped person at the controls of the pony without severely restricting the speed and the area in which the pony could perform. Very stringent – and very valid – safety precautions and rules were laid down to ensure, as far as is humanly possible where horses are concerned, minimal risk to the partakers. Hence it was essential that there were two sets of reins and two drivers, vital that the disabled person was loaded last and unloaded first, important to have an adequate number of ground helpers to be at the pony's head and assist with the loading and so on.

It was also decreed that outside the confines of an indoor arena, which was by far the safest environment for driving for the disabled to take place, every disabled turnout had to be accompanied by helpers on foot or on bicycle. The

logic and the safety value of this was unquestionable, but
the reality of it was very frustrating. To begin with we had
no indoor school, all of our group's activities had to take
place either out in our less than perfect field or out on the
roads and lanes surrounding Stanley Crook. Anyone even
remotely familiar with our locality knows one word that
can sum it up: hilly.

This meant that our 'on foot' helpers, not being of the
trained Olympic variety, were often red-faced and knocking at the knees after the shortest of excursions, and even
attempts at 'bicycle outriders' didn't prove much more of
a success when Billy Row Bank rivals anything the Tour
de France has to offer! Slow, sedate toddles around the
immediate back streets became the order of the day – but
also quickly became very boring. This led to 'plan B', which
was to form a convoy for the ponies when out driving by
putting motor cars with helpers inside at the front and
rear of the ponies, vigilantly watching for the pre-arranged
signal for a driver in trouble: a whip held vertically in the
air above the head.

At least this way we found we could trot for a decent
distance without giving heart attacks for our on-foot or on-
bicycle support team. But we were to find we had the
opposite problem in that little ponies pulling carriages with
two adults in, had not got the horsepower of motor cars,
and often we could hear whinings and rumblings of badly
over-heating engines as the cars crawled along in first gear
behind the little cavalcade.

By 1987 the group had grown modestly in members and
impressively in equipment. Although we still possessed
our original 'Jubilee' cart we were now the proud owners
of two purpose-built carriages that were real feats of engineering. Not only was the 'Jubilee' cart uncomfortable and
very basic, it *looked* like an invalid carriage. It was too wide
and too low and too *different* ever to resemble a traditional
horse-drawn vehicle. Quite rightly, our drivers began to

ask why they should not be able to drive out in carriages that had the minimum possible modifications from the norm. Why did they have to be restricted to something clumsy, low and unattractive?

With the same spirit that I suspect swept away the little one-person three-wheeler 'invalid cars' once much in evidence on the road in favour of a normal car with steering or foot control modifications, the group set about putting matters to rights. A great deal of money was raised by grants and fund-raising events and by much rattling of tins. A Yorkshire engineer called Norman Brown was given the task of designing what the group so passionately wanted – a carriage with as near as possible traditional lines and large traditional wheels, but into which it was also possible to load a wheelchair, and one that was, above all else, stable and safe to drive across a variety of terrains – including open ground.

By the late autumn of 1987 our dream was fulfilled. We had taken delivery of our 'Ruskin Rambler', a beautiful carriage of natural varnished wood resplendent with dark maroon wheels and metalwork. It had gleaming brass fittings, had a choice of seating to suit ambulant or wheelchair disabled, and once the cunningly concealed ramp was stowed away beneath the floor, very little distinguished the carriage from a 'normal' vehicle. It was beautiful.

Its arrival coincided – by fate or good fortune – with another major development within the disabled carriage driving world. All year the debate had raged back and forth at meetings and seminars and at group and national level. In the end, the loudest voice was that of disabled drivers themselves who said, quite plainly, *why* are we so limited in what we are allowed to do? *Why* can we compete in dressage tests and cone driving tests but not be allowed to do marathon or cross-country? *Why* can't we drive hazards? If it's not 'safe' for us to do so, why can't hazards be designed which *are* safe for us? *Why* can't we have events with all three disciplines – just like able-bodied competitors, just like normal people?

The advent of the Nostell Priory event in October 1987 saw the death throes of the 'red flag' syndrome. Alice Wynn, a tireless and enthusiastic worker on behalf of driving for the disabled, was not only organizer of a disabled group in Yorkshire, she was also an ex-competitor herself, a driver in that most masochistic of classes, the tandem class. Alice epitomized everything a well-bred English country lady should be, and beneath her 'pearls and green gum boots' exterior beat a warm, charitable and determined heart. From her large but delightfully lived-in country seat at Alby Park, she chaired many a spirited meeting of all the RDA driving groups in the north and laid the finishing touches to her master plan: a proper one-day event for disabled drivers at Nostell near Wakefield, with Presentation and Dressage and Cone driving. And a marathon – with *hazards*.

Loud were the mutterings, loud were the murmurings, grave were the shakings of some heads. But great was the rejoicing, frantic the preparations and intense the training at Stanley Crook.

We were in actual fact looking for a bigger, stronger pony to drive our new 'super vehicle'. Poor Bobby was quite frankly just too small for a carriage that, in order to fit the specifications of its design, had to be larger, higher and heavier than its Jubilee predecessor. Nevertheless, when the choice was put to Heather Stoddart to drive the Jubilee or the Ruskin – even if it meant going slower in the Ruskin because of the weight problem for Bobby – the answer, roughly translated, was that she wouldn't be seen *dead* in the Jubilee cart. So Heather, driving Bobby in the Ruskin and assisted by myself, and Brenda, driving Glint assisted by Hazel in her own vehicle, became the entries for the Nostell Priory event.

Harness was polished, carts were polished, ponies were

polished. Heather's husband, Colin, even gave her wheel-chair the once over. Driving aprons were made and engaging co-ordinating headgear was invested in. Gloves, whips, lamps – all oh-so-familiar paraphernalia and preparation for a driving event went on in the yard. But this time with a new and different purpose in view.

Finally, the big day: ponies and vehicles were loaded into the horsebox; people, wheelchairs, picnic hampers and harness, were loaded into cars – and away we went. There were some half a dozen groups from the north represented there that day, their members competing against each other with a wide range of disabilities from paraplegia, polio, cerebral palsy though to Down's syndrome and even one blind driver. Heather was the only tetraplegic there.

She looked radiant in her maroon hat and white blouse. The weather was perfect – warm, golden late-October sun shone off multi-coloured leaves and the mirrored glistening chestnuts that kept my daughter Megan and Heather's twin boys busy all day collecting them by the bucketful. The elegant stately façade of the Priory itself presided benignly over the goings on on the front lawn.

George and Marjorie were every inch the proud owners, leading Bobby round resplendent in a little pale blue rug Marjorie had made for him, complete with his name on one side and George's initials on the other. His palomino coat had been brushed until it looked like gold satin and his blonde mane and tail shone with love and shampoo. Suddenly it was time to put it all together and on went the harness, and into the shafts went Bobby. I was in position next, and Heather, as the rule book decreed, was loaded last. Then the ramp was up and tucked away, shoulder and leg harness was adjusted to make sure we didn't lose Heather and the next minute Bobby was heading off for the judging area for presentation, his little black hooves glistening with oil as he toddled along the path. The presentation went very well – the Judge did comment that the carriage was on the large side for a pony, but that we knew already.

Next came dressage; not the best test ever driven, but Heather was so pleased simply to have remembered the test that her joy was quite infectious.

And then . . . the marathon. Now, I knew it wasn't *really* a marathon – a real driven marathon is after all in the region of seventeen miles. This was more like four miles. But four miles for a very small pony with a very heavy cart *is* a marathon task. Particularly when there are hazards to face at the end of it.

'Now then,' the Course Marshal had said to us on our arrival, 'you can walk all the hazards to your heart's content, or,' he added smiling to Heather, 'drive round them in your car, but about the water hazard . . .'

Water hazard? *Water* hazard!

I felt a momentary panic: Bobby had never driven through water in his life as far as I knew. How deep was it? How wide was it? What if he refused? What if he shied? What if we tipped up?

'. . . it is purely optional. No penalties will be added if you miss it out. We realize that a lot of the disabled drivers will never have tackled anything like this before, so it's unfair to make it compulsory. There is another route, only slightly longer, over the bridge, if you would prefer to take that.'

Was this such a good idea after all, I asked myself as we set off to 'walk' the course.

The hazards had actually been designed very, very carefully and were a credit to the event. Most were constructed of the new type of huge round bales of straw. These provided reasonably immovable elements which were nevertheless fairly forgiving if one did crunch into them. All the hazards were on good, flat ground and there was no camber to tip up a cart. All the hazards were manned by a group of volunteers, all ready to dive in and help if anyone got into the slightest bit of difficulty. They were, however, still *hazards*. They had complicated routes that had to be remembered and fairly tight turns to take and, as they were against the clock, speed was going to be an important factor.

The water hazard, the first to be tackled on the course, did not seem all that formidable: not for someone out riding cross-country. Not for Richard with the pair who would have hopped and splashed across the little six-inch deep stream in three or four strides. But for a little pony to come down a grassy slope with a heavy cart and two people behind him, face running water for the first time in his life and then up the bank on the other side and out . . . I had my doubts. Colin had parked the car as near to the stream as he could to allow Heather to have as close a look as possible. She surveyed it all carefully.

I bent down beside the open passenger window. 'You don't have to drive it you know, Heather,' I said reassuringly. 'That's why it's optional; for people who have never driven through water before. I don't suppose Bobby would do anything but . . . you never know and it might be safer to keep straight on over the bridge rather than coming down that bank.'

Heather brought her gaze up level to mine. 'I would rather,' she stated, 'drive the water hazard, if it's all right with you.'

'You're the competitor,' I smiled back with a confidence I certainly didn't feel and, later in the day, rattling and banging alarmingly down the bankside towards that suddenly menacing stretch of water, my brain screamed, 'My God! What am I doing! Am I out of my mind? I'm in this contraption with a paralysed woman who is strapped to a wheelchair. If we tip over she can't be thrown out – she could be killed! Perhaps we could both be killed! This pony has never done this before . . .'

'Come on Bobby! Come on!' yelled Heather.

'. . . and neither has Heather,' I reminded myself. 'Steady up a bit, Heather!' I cautioned urgently. 'Don't hit the water too fast: if he suddenly refuses we could be in real trouble here!'

'Bobby won't refuse, will you Bobby!' Heather replied.

'Well, go steady anyway or you'll break your ruddy neck!' It was out before I thought. Off the tongue in a flash and then hanging, reverberating in the air. I withered and curled inside; I particularly longed for the earth to swallow me.

Heather smiled back warmly, 'I've already tried that!' she said. 'And I've not got a lot to lose, have I? Come on Bobby! Clever lad!'

Without a second's hesitation, Bobby trotted into the water and suddenly we were both yelling as he flashed valiantly through.

'Come on, come on, come on!'

Colin was in the car on the opposite side waving his hat and cheering. Our girl grooms strategically placed near at hand in case of any trouble were jumping and whooping in the unanimous cry of 'Come on Bobby!'

Six, seven, eight strides, then head down and straining into his collar the sturdy little chap pulled us up the opposite bank to cheers and claps and whistles.

'Trot on Bobby – trot on,' sang Heather happily, and trot on he did.

He must have been very tired and I will never know quite what lifted him: the novelty, the adrenalin or simply some sort of knowing. But he gave and he gave. In and out, between the bales, between the trees. Lifting every time to Heather's voice – to Heather's hands. And I realized, stunned and humbled, that it was Heather's hands – with minimal help from me – that were guiding Bobby through the elements of the hazards. The only reason she really needed my hands was as brakes, as she couldn't really shorten the reins herself. And brakes were not featuring high on the agenda that afternoon.

The fourth hazard, the last and then up through the slalom and towards the finish line.

'Go on Bobby, go! Go!' Heather yelled, her faced flushed and more totally alive than I'd ever seen it.

'Red flags on the right!' I reminded her, quite unnecessarily I was sure.

'It's okay, I remembered,' she laughed back and, hands extending further and more actively than I'd ever seen her achieve before, she steered, left, right, left then right again. 'Go Bobby, go on! Clever lad. Nearly there! Go on!'

From heaven alone knows where, the little chap stretched out legs that must have been more tired than he had ever known and to rapturous applause we were over the line and I was finally pulling him up to a halt.

Eyes bright with moisture and face flushed with excitement and achievement, Heather was glowing with pride. 'That was ... oh that was ...' she tried to say.

And then I saw Colin standing beside her; all the concern and worry that he had had etched on his face before Heather had set off now gone, but not replaced with anything as simple as relief. On Colin's face there was to be plainly read something reaching beyond pride and into pure wonder.

I thought it had been a good year for our horses; I thought the National Championship for the second time was an unbeatable achievement. But, in all honesty, sitting in that little cart with a small sweaty pony and a paralysed friend, I felt a joy and a fulfilment I had never thought possible.

We didn't win the event by a long shot – though Hazel and Brenda won the marathon with Glint and missed the overall prize, the magnificent silver George Bowman trophy, by only one point.

But we did win something that day that was priceless. In the last of the afternoon sun, in the last act of our driving year, Bobby Dazzler, the pony that we'd so nearly lost and given up hope on, and Heather Stoddart, who had nearly done the same with her own life, had come through together to collect their rosettes, collect their applause and collect my undying admiration and humble thanks for allowing me to share in their very personal victory. The red flag had been flattened from behind: one-day events for the disabled were no longer a debating point, a dream. They were a reality that Heather and Bobby had just helped to prove. The road ahead lay clear.

10

When God Slams the Door

My Great-aunt Meg, God rest her soul, used to have a rather pessimistic view on Providence and the good Lord's bounty. Life, in her experience, went more along the lines of 'God never closes one door but he slams another in your face!' Had I listened long and hard at the start of the 1988 season would I have heard the trembling of door frames I wondered? Certainly had I been allowed to glimpse through the door at the beginning of the year into what lay ahead by the end of it I would have simply closed it quietly and tiptoed away, hoping not to be noticed.

On the face of it the omens were good: we had our third year of sponsorship from Montan, the weather was staying marvellously mild and open which meant we could work the horses to our heart's content. We had had staff changes, having parted company with Heather Baldwin. Richard and she had never truly struck up a good working relationship and I supposed that Alastair was an impossible act to follow. She was too young, too far from home and not experienced enough to really take charge of the YTS girls and the yard. Sharon had also left at the end of her two-year training period and so we started the year with an almost total staff change – new YTS trainees and one Helen Swainsten as head groom. She was a very lucky find: a qualified AI living locally enough to travel to us daily without living in. She was a breath of fresh air – very lightly built with dark curly hair and very quiet and reserved in herself, but mustard with the horses on the yard and on their backs and a good teacher for the trainees.

Our first win of the season, at Islabank in Perth, was our first ever hat-trick of winning a major event for three years in succession. Our pleasure over the victory was soon dampened however when we tried to leave for the next event at Holker Hall, only to discover that the gearbox and the back axle of the horsebox had disintegrated. We were stranded in Scotland for three days and only just made it into the arena at Holker to do our dressage at 9.00 am, having travelled all through the previous night. We lost the event to Christine Dick by half a point and then reversed this result at Tatton Park in Cheshire a few weeks later by beating her by a whisker. We were high in contention for the National Points League Championships, we were the reigning National Champions with our title to defend in what could make a hat-trick year in a couple of months' time. We had good sponsors, good horses and good health. I wasn't so foolish as to allow myself to feel invincible, but for the first time in many long and anxious years I felt that the clouds had finally rolled back and I could allow myself to luxuriate in the sunshine of life.

Suddenly it was August. Early August meant only one thing in the strange yearly cycle of our lives: Lowther.

To give it its full title, it was the Lowther Country Fair and Horse Driving Trials, held in the grounds of Lowther Castle Estate near Penrith. But 'Lowther' sufficed for all we associated with the event: a gruelling Lake District course, demanding hazards, very often appalling, rainy weather and a track record of bad luck that stretched back for Richard over many years. True, the previous year we had finally broken that depressing record when we came second for Alan Robson and Montan – and in unusually sunny weather. But, as they say, it takes more than one swallow to make a summer, and the residual effect of many years of broken vehicles, errors of judgement and problems with horses had not left me predisposed to looking forward to Lowther.

The draught that had begun creeping round the door at the start of the year suddenly began whistling round my ankles when Alan Robson asked to see Richard and me for a private meeting. Our relationship with Alan over the three years of sponsorship had developed into one of warmth and respectful informality; to be 'summoned' to a formal meeting set the hair-trigger on my internal alarm.

He was, he informed us without preamble, selling Montan. Before our respective jaws dropped to their full extent, he quickly added that, *however*, the company he was selling to were quite intrigued by the 'Horse Driving thing', and Alan had pointed out the many worthwhile benefits it had brought to Montan. They were, however, entirely ignorant of the whole procedure and Alan had therefore invited a large delegation, including the Chairman of his new parent company, to Lowther to see what it was all about. As for Richard's job with the transport section of Montan, that too would be perfectly secure. In fact, with the envisaged increase in production and distribution, there would be more work then ever. The new owners of Montan were a large London-based financial group which had already bought a northern company that manufactured shop fittings. They hoped to align it with Montan to produce a formidable force in the northern shop-fitting world.

While I was very touched by Alan's obvious concern and hard work to ensure a continuity of sponsorship and income for us, with that decision moving out of his personal control, I couldn't help wishing that, somehow, it was to be at an event less ill-starred than Lowther.

The importance of the event lent it an urgency that I did not enjoy. Richard drove a passable dressage test, but not one of his best and it left him several points behind Christine. It was the worst possible position to be in – not in contention and not far enough behind to say 'Oh well, I don't stand an earthly chance of catching her, so I may as well just go steady and do as well as I can'. It meant that he was going to have to cut every corner, take every even vaguely calculated risk, push the horses to their very utmost. In short, to go like hell.

Marathon day dawned hot and sunny: too hot, too sunny. By mid-day temperatures were in the 80s and it was being pronounced the hottest day of the year. The thermometer and my stress levels rose simultaneously. Trying to console myself with the fact that it was just as hot for everyone else in the class didn't seem to help much at all. As usual, after Richard left to commence the marathon course, I was left to the dreadful inertia of waiting out nearly two hours until he completed the rest of the course and came into the hazards. Then I could allow myself to get *really* uptight.

I filled in the vacuum with various potterings and organizing the refreshments for the assembled company when they returned from viewing the fray. Various friends popped in to chat, which helped, and I did have Bear there to keep me company – though I don't think he was best pleased at not being out on the marathon. Two of the visitors were the parents of one of our grooms, Jo. She was busy getting beds down and warm water for Heather and Blizzard's return but found time to show her parents round and, of course, take them to say hello to Bear. The conversation turned, as it inevitably did, to the awful scars on his hindquarters.

'My goodness, he's certainly been through it, hasn't he?' said Jo's mum. 'And I hear you've had a pretty rough time of it too, what with riding accidents and a broken pelvis and the like. It's a wonder you have the nerve to go on with it any more at all.'

'Ah well,' I replied, with one of those fatally blasé statements that we so often throw in the face of Providence. 'Thank God all those disasters and accidents are well behind us now.'

I was watching as Richard approached hazard six. It had large upright posts, immovably sunk into the ground. It was not one that had particularly worried Richard, nor one of which I had taken any particular notice. It was sort of – well – ordinary somehow. The horses were negotiating it smoothly enough; they certainly weren't taking terribly tight turns, nor going through it, from my distance anyway, at a particularly fast pace. 'Oh God' ran the only thoughts in my mind, 'don't say they are tiring. Not yet, please not yet, just another ten minutes or so, that's all they need. Four more hazards and they're home. Don't let them slow down! And don't let them boil over! Come on, Richard, come on!'

From one stride to the next, in merely the time it took for the eye to register that forward movement had ceased, the carriage and the horses stopped. There was no noise, no crunch. Nothing. One stride and they were moving forward, the next they had come to a dead halt. But Richard hadn't.

An intake of breath, a sharp gasp rustled along the watching crowd like wind shaking a line of trees, as all those scores of eyes watched Richard lift out of his seat, go out of the vehicle and reappear, some scant seconds that felt like several lifetimes later, beside the rearside wheel.

He was sitting on the ground facing backwards to the cart beside Blizzard's hind legs; his reins miraculously and yet somehow ludicrously still gripped in his hands. Never let go of the reins, preached Richard; whatever else happens, never let go of those reins.

Along with the reins he was hanging grimly on to a

handful of Blizzard's red tail. I was on my feet, gripping
the rope that separated the crowd from the hazard where
all eyes were now focused. There was a terrible, awful,
tearing anguish in me over what to do: my instinct said
run, run and see if he's all right, run and find out what
has happened. But a cold, logical voice was overriding this
instinct saying, perhaps there's *nothing* the matter; perhaps
he's just winded; Helen is at the horses' heads and they're
not going anywhere. If you – or anyone else – go to interfere now, it would be deemed as outside assistance and
he'll be eliminated. The cold and hardened voice concerned
only with the successful completion of this most vital of
events was actually urging impatiently, 'Come on Richard,
get up! Get back on that cart; for God's sake don't get
eliminated – get up!'

As Richard took a firmer grip of Blizzard's tail, I watched
dry-mouthed he began slowly to pull himself up from
the ground where he sat. His scream ripped across the
intervening space to hit me like a physical blow. Then I
was running; running faster than I knew it was possible
for me to run, so quickly was I there that it seemed that
the scream and my reaching him were barely separated.
His eyes were screwed up, tightly closed in reaction against
the brilliant sunshine and the agony that was clearly etched
on his face. I was unsure if he was even conscious.

Then, very softly, his voice left barely moving lips, 'My
leg. Oh my God, my leg.'

I realized that, since I had reached him, my eyes had
scanned only his face. Now I allowed them to travel down
his body. There was something odd and ominous about
the way his right leg lay on the grass; something to do
with the way it was bent. Could the articulation of his
knee in any way account for that extraordinary angle? No,
I realized, suddenly sickened, the bend was not at his knee:
it was lower, much lower.

We had joked many times over the choice of wearing

bright red tracksuit trousers to do the marathon course. The choice was, in reality, to complement our Montan team colours: red and white hats, grey jumpers and red trousers. But, one wit had pointed out, it was a good colour for hiding the blood stains. Well, he was wrong.

The wet sticky stain that was spreading across the fabric was of an altogether darker shade of red.

The sense of unreality, of the total suspension of time and place and the evidence of my eyes, was at its height. I knew I should react, do something, even if it were only to panic and scream for help. But I was frozen into immobility. It was as if I had merged completely with that immobile figure lying on the grass under that clear blue sky – reliving the sensation of almost blessed detachment that comes in the brief interlude between the occurrence of a horrific injury and the body's full reaction to it. Thank God, I had said, thank God all the injuries and disasters now lay behind us: less than an hour in real time had elapsed since I had flaunted that arrogant statement in the face of Providence. Well, God, I thought bitterly, the door to destiny has been closing slowly on us all year – now it's well and truly slammed shut.

Richard stirred and moaned slightly beside me. Instantly the world snapped back into focus and on to real time. I became aware of people running, of the noise of voices, the crackle of walkie-talkies, the sound of vehicles approaching at speed. I don't suppose much more than ten seconds had elapsed since I first reached him, yet so many thoughts and so many memories had flooded through me. Now, from a timeless dimension where all things had seemed briefly suspended, everything was suddenly happening in fast forward.

'An ambulance is coming!' a voice above and to the side of me announced.

Richard groaned and stirred more strongly, his hand

searching for mine. I intertwined my fingers with his. 'It's all right – help's coming. Just hang on.'

This news seemed to have the opposite effect to reassuring him and his head rolled from side to side on the ground. I grasped his hand the tighter, remembering how the arrival of the ambulance had marked a moment of terror for me; the terror of having broken bones moved, the terror of unknown heights of pain. I wondered if these very same fears were now assailing Richard. 'It's all right,' I tried to reassure him. 'They'll give you something for the pain.'

By now he lay in the centre of a pool of activity. Officials shouted and bustled, I was aware of the sounds of horses being unharnessed, even vaguely aware of Helen's tearful voice asking for news. All that circus bustled around us and I knew there were hundreds of eyes straining towards the drama being enacted out in the centre of hazard six. I longed to get him away, provide some privacy.

Someone uttered the magic word 'doctor', and I looked up to see a slightly out of breath gentleman who had obviously run across from the waiting crowd. 'I don't suppose there's anything I can do,' he said, apologetically, 'I don't have my bag with me. It's locked in the car in the car park – and a lot of damned use it is there.'

'It's his right leg!' I informed him; a piece of news that was unnecessary even for the untrained eye.

'Mmm, looks like a nasty compound fracture. Can't see too much for the tracksuit and I don't want to interfere with it. Damn. I just wish I could give him something for the pain.'

A white vehicle braked suddenly, doors slammed, and two men in black uniforms appeared with a stretcher. The insignia on their vehicle and uniform said St John Ambulance Brigade.

My heart sank. Where was the ambulance, the *real* ambulance? Weren't these people part-time volunteers or something? How could they possibly help someone as badly injured as Richard?

They conferred briefly with the doctor and then knelt down beside me on the grass. After a quick confab, during which they seemed to barely touch the injured leg, one ambulanceman got up and ran over to the official with the walkie-talkie radio, whilst the other one turned to talk to me. 'Are you with this gentleman? Will you be going with him to the hospital?'

'I'm his wife. Which hospital are you taking him to?'

'We won't be actually taking him to the hospital.'

'But he needs . . .' I began to protest.

'Not all the way,' he hastily reassured me. 'You see, we're only St John's – on duty here on the showfield – we need a County ambulance to get him to Carlisle.

'Carlisle!' I was stunned. 'Surely that's a very long way away: isn't there a hospital in Penrith?'

'Not to deal with a fracture as bad as this appears to be. Best for him to go where they can do a proper job, eh?'

I was trembling now, shaking as the horror and the reality of it all began to bite for the first time. I must have looked as awful as I felt because the ambulanceman was now scanning my face with concern.

'It'll not be long,' he reassured me, holding me firmly by the arm. 'We've radioed for it and we're going to meet up with it at a small village just outside the showfield and then we'll have your husband off to Carlisle in a crack. It's not that far you know – only about twenty miles.'

'But his leg . . . the pain . . .' I was close to giving way now, visions of Richard being heaved in and out of vehicles in agony.

'We're going to immobilize his leg in a cradle splint and, although we can't give him any of the real hard stuff, we do have gas and air with us; that'll take the edge off the pain for him, I promise you.'

And, sure enough, when I turned back to Richard, the

first St John's man was holding a cylinder with a mask on close to Richard's mouth while the doctor was trying to move his leg as gently as possible into the waiting splint.

'You'll be all right now?' the ambulanceman with me asked. 'I'm just going to give him a hand – the sooner we're away the better.'

I nodded, numbed and frightened.

Take the edge off the pain the gas may have done, but it was a thin edge. Another scream, strangled and gurgling into the rubber mask pressed tightly around his mouth and nose, tore from Richard as his leg was lifted and as swiftly as possible straightened into the waiting cradle.

The sky reeled and I cried out involuntarily in response, feeling helpless, useless, sickened. An arm came up beneath my elbow and gripped me firmly. 'What can I do to help?'

'Alan! Oh Alan!' I sobbed in a mixture of relief and regret. 'Why did this have to happen? *Why*? And why today? I'm so sorry we've let you down.'

'Don't be stupid! It's us that's worried about you – how can you possibly have let us down?' He scribbled something on a piece of paper and pushed it into my top pocket. 'Here's the car-phone number – I'll have someone listening by it at all times. As soon as there is news or when you want a lift back here, phone and I'll send a car for you. All right?'

'Yes, Alan. Thank you.'

I followed the stretcher bearing Richard into the ambulance. Framed by the small square window in the ambulance door was the stark and simple picture of the tragedy that had befallen us. The cross-country vehicle stood where it had come to such a sudden and devastating halt at hazard six. No horses now, no driver. Just a mass of metal and wood lying there, empty – accusing even. Though not alive itself, it was indeed the host for the living entities that attached themselves to and on to it. The two strong and willing horses that gave movement to its wheels, Richard's hands giving purpose to its direction, Helen's weight and skill giving balance and manoeuvrability to the whole. The almost awesome 'coming together' of people, horses and carriages. Scant minutes previously they'd been whole, they had been one.

Even as I watched the picture fall back into the distance, that entity should have been labouring back to camp, up the Lowther hill to a relieved welcome, a well deserved rest. Instead, the whole lay fragmented, scattered: the horses bemused and puzzled at being led home, slack traces dangling around their hocks; the vehicle awaiting the somehow demeaning fate of having to be towed away by a Land-Rover. And Richard – Richard lying there pale and broken.

Dear God, the thought pierced me like a spike, would there ever be a coming together again? Would I ever want there to be?

Despite the best endeavours of the driver, the ambulance lurched across a deeply rutted patch of field. It caused Richard to groan loudly and grasp the metal rail that held his stretcher securely in place till his knuckles were white.

'How much further?' I asked anxiously.

'Not far now,' came back the reply. 'Nearly off this damned field, then surfaced roads to the rendezvous point.'

Sure enough, with a final juddering rattle the ambulance suddenly reached tarmac and began to negotiate the narrow, twisting road down to the village. Only the empty eye sockets of the tower windows in the ruins of Lowther Castle were left to watch as we made our retreat from our field of battle.

The transfer to the County ambulance was quick and professional. The driver – to my surprise – was a small, slightly built lady in her thirties. I had never thought of myself as being sexist – 'the woman's role' and so on. I was, after all, a modern woman, an educated woman, a working woman. But there was a vague disquiet in me that I simply couldn't rationalize, caused by the small female form behind the driving wheel and the two bulkier masculine forms attending to Richard. As we cleared the village roads and came to the junction leading to the M6, my faith in my own gender was about to be put to the ultimate test.

'Don't be alarmed by the noise,' she shouted breezily over her shoulder. 'The siren's just to get people out of the way and get us there as quickly as possible. It's only about twenty miles, so we'll not be long. Hang on!'

The noise and the acceleration hit me simultaneously. This really was a siren, a siren that blasted in blatant American tones, first a batch of staccato notes and then a long drawn out wail. We were in the outside lane in moments. I didn't dare even glance at the speedometer, but I knew I had never, ever, driven at that speed in my life.

Screeching and screaming its warning, the siren cleared any cars ahead of us as if by magic, and any car that failed to give way to that monstrous, flashing, wailing shape bearing down upon it would have been foolish indeed.

The effect of the siren and the speed momentarily diverted my anxiety and thoughts away from Richard. Any error, the tiniest error, at that speed and we were all surely dead. At least the road was straight and we were of course free of oncoming traffic. I might indeed yet live to make it to the hospital.

In an indecently short space of time the sign announcing the turn-off for Carlisle loomed up and then flashed past. As our driver swung off the motorway on to the slip road she slammed the brakes on with such intensity that the entire vehicle juddered and shook. At least, I breathed more deeply and evenly, we would not be able to go at that speed through the town. And indeed we didn't. Well, not quite.

Actually the effect of rarely going below sixty in the middle of a built-up area was, I discovered, trebly more alarming than going at over a hundred on the motorway. For one thing there were bends – corners even. Round-abouts, traffic lights and, most alarming of all, traffic moving in both directions. Somehow, I shall never know how, the traffic retreated – fled even – at the approach of the howling white terror. Cars seemed to throw themselves off the roads on to pavements, nearly through shop windows. At various points at least two police cars aided and abetted our dash through the town, and after we had swung contemptuously right at traffic lights that plainly said red, I realized somewhat ashamedly that my knees were knocking over the intact passage of my *own* body, rather than the safe arrival of Richard's. Stone gates and iron railings loomed into view and flower beds and a large glass-canopied parking bay.

Throughout the journey to the hospital, the only real movement had been the headlong dash of the ambulance itself. Inside the vehicle there had been little activity, simply regular checks on Richard's pulse and breathing. Little talking, little movement.

Now, suddenly, activity erupted all around us. Doors were flung open and the stretcher was out and on to a trolley before I had time to clamber out myself. I wanted to say some word of thanks to our driver for her literally breathtaking high-speed skill, but I caught only a glimpse of her petite figure disappearing into a separate door before I had to virtually trot alongside Richard's trolley as we whirled along a painted corridor. Then we were into an area with rows of curtained cubicles. A nurse very kindly but quite firmly said to me, 'Just wait over there a minute please,' as the trolley disappeared from my view behind enclosing drapes.

I sat obediently on the little hard chair against the wall, trying to fight down the sensations of panic and real fear that were sweeping through me. Eyes closed, trying to breathe deeply and slowly, trying to dispel the nausea and light-headedness that had suddenly come over me. Time passed, but it was immeasurable. It could have been moments, it could have been eternity.

'Mrs Smith?'

My eyes shot open to behold a nurse bending slightly anxiously over me. 'Yes!'

'Are you all right?'

'Oh yes, just – well the shock, I expect.'

'Your husband's a lot more comfortable now; he's had a shot for the pain and the doctor's examined him. They've taken him down to X-ray to find out what needs to be done. Would you like to go down there and wait with him?'

'Yes, of course. Where do I go?' I was on my feet suddenly, too suddenly I regretted when the room began to swim slightly. I felt disoriented, lost in an unknown environment.

'You are in casualty now,' the nurse informed me. 'If you just follow that red line on the floor out of that door, it will take you right to X-ray. Are you sure you're all right? Would you like me to come with you?'

'Oh no, don't worry about me: I'm sure you're much too busy here. Even I can't go wrong with directions like that.'

I thanked her and headed off through the indicated door, clinging with eyes and feet to the scarlet strip that flowed like an artery along the floor, my only tenuous lifeline to Richard. It wound eventually into another large waiting area and there I found him, draped now with a white cotton blanket.

That the burden of the worst of the pain had been lifted was immediately apparent. Gone were the deeply drawn lines around his mouth and eyes, and his hands lay unclenched beside him on the trolley. He was conscious, although obviously very drowsy, and he smiled slowly at me when I peered down anxiously at him. 'How is it now?'

'Better. Much better.'

'They're going to do X-rays now, but I expect they've told you that, and then – well, then we'll have to wait and see what they suggest, won't we? You'll probably get a walloping great pot on your leg and everyone will want to sign it!'

'The horses – what's happened to the horses?'

'They are fine. Perfectly fine.' I took his hand and squeezed it. 'They weren't hurt at all in any way when you crashed or whatever. Helen will have them long since tucked up in bed with their teas. There is honestly nothing to worry about. Alan has already seen me and you know that he will have everything well under control.'

'What ever *did* happen? That's the question, Carol, I can't honestly remember! One moment I was flying through the gates and suddenly I was flying through the air. The next thing I remember was sitting on the ground beside Blizzard and then I tried to get up and ... and ...' Whether with remembered or present pain, the thought made him tense and flinch slightly.

'Don't worry about all that now; don't even *think* about it. We've all the time in the world to sort that out when we get *you* sorted out. Now just try to relax and lie there like a good boy, or they'll be sending me away for upsetting you.'

I became aware of an alarming sense of weakness somewhere around four o'clock that afternoon. I suddenly remembered that, too busy and too uptight over the approaching marathon, I had skipped breakfast. I had intended eating well and heartily with the guests in the marquee after the completion of the marathon. But of course, it was never completed. So, apart from one early morning cup of tea, I had had nothing to eat or drink since the previous night. I began to snooze at my station alongside Richard's trolley.

'We're going up to the ward to admit your husband now,' a kind voice brought me wide awake suddenly. 'The doctor will come and have a word with you there.'

'Thank you, thank you very much,' I replied, as once again I tagged along behind the trolley. Admit him? I thought, well, if he had to have an anaesthetic to set the leg they would have to admit him . . .

'. . . So you see,' the doctor peered intently at the shadowy picture on the screen in the little side room of the ward, 'it's a very complicated and severe fracture. It's not so much *a* break, as a series of breaks – actually, "crushed" would be the best description. The break in the fibula – that's the thinner bone at the back of the leg – is not so serious: it's not a weight-bearing bone. But the tibia,' he pointed with his forefinger, 'that's broken diagonally here above,' he pointed once more, 'and broken diagonally here below, leaving . . .' he jabbed finally and emphatically, 'this triangular piece of bone almost floating free in the middle of his leg.'

Though extremely grateful for the doctor's long and careful explanation and a chance to see the X-ray, I didn't really need my 'A' level Human Biology to know that the bones of the lower leg should not resemble the jigsaw picture that I was staring at. 'What is the procedure for a break like this?' I asked, trying desperately to sound as controlled and professional as the doctor had been to me.

'Well, a plaster cast is out of the question. For one thing, where the bones have penetrated the flesh will need stitching, and for another a cast just wouldn't hold these bones anywhere near tight enough for them to knit. Fortunately, we have a surgeon here who has trained in a relatively new and unique approach to bone injuries. It was developed by a specialist from your part of the world – County Durham, isn't it?'

'Yes, that's right.'

'The device is called a Fixator. It looks rather like a shock absorber, to be honest, and what it does is to act like an external bone, taking the weight-bearing off the real bones and putting tension on them to hold them together at the same time.'

'You say this device is external? How is it fixed to the leg then?'

'It isn't fixed to the leg – it's fixed *into* the leg: screwed into the bone in fact.'

'Screwed into the bone? From the *outside*?' My horrified and rapidly paling face obviously betrayed my thought process.

'Sounds horrendous, I know. Actually it looks far worse than it feels to the patient, the bone itself has no nerve endings you know. Once in place, you hardly know it's there.'

'And when do you propose to do this operation?'

'We're clearing the decks now: all being well he'll be going down to theatre at about 6.00 pm. Any other questions you would like to ask?'

'No, thank you. I'll go back and see him now, if I may.'

I sank wearily into the chair beside Richard's bed. My legs really did feel like jelly and my head was lighter than ever.

'Are you sure you're all right?' the second nurse of the afternoon asked me.

'I think so. It's probably just the shock, and I'm so very thirsty: I'd give my right arm for a cup of tea.'

Instantly realizing what a tactless thing that was to say in an orthopaedic ward I felt wretched, but the nurse smiled warmly. 'No need to do anything that drastic. I'll go and get you one right away. When did you last eat by the way?'

'Not since last night.'

'Well no wonder you're feeling light-headed! I'll not be a few minutes.'

Sure enough she was soon back bearing a tray with a large pot of tea and a plate on which reposed four triangles of toast, all warm and buttery. Saliva instantly flooded my previously parched mouth and from my mid-region a loud and urgent gurgle issued.

'You'll feel better after that,' she said cheerfully, and she was right. I savoured every morsel of the toast and even licked the butter from my fingertips. I drank the tea in thankful draughts, feeling it warm and revive me.

'Did you enjoy that?' a slurred voice asked. 'I could murder for just a mouthful of that tea.'

'Richard! I thought you were asleep.' I felt guilty, not actually because I was eating or drinking, but because I was enjoying it so much.

'Just dozing. They tell me they're going to operate tonight – gave me something to sign. God knows what – I could have agreed for them to take my leg off for all I know!'

'Richard! Don't *say* things like that, even for a joke.' I didn't know how much he had been told, or how much he was in a fit state to understand anyway, so I decided against going into details with him. 'They're going to set it. You're going to have a general anaesthetic – that's why you can't have anything to eat or drink.'

He nodded in understanding and assent. 'How are you getting back?' was his next question.

'Alan told me to phone and he'd send a car for me. But it could be very late tonight before I can do that.'

'Well, phone now. Get your lift.'

'I'm not going till you're back from theatre,' I protested.

'Listen, I'd be happier with you back with the horses. God knows when I'll actually get down for this operation, and God knows how long I'll be. It's not fair to be dragging people out late at night to collect you now, is it?'

'But . . .' my lower lip trembled.

'But nothing. I've never had an operation before but you've had more than your fair share. What did you say to me when you were in Shotley Bridge? "Please don't come and see me till the day after – I always feel so awful till the anaesthetic wears off". Well, it could be tomorrow morning before I even know where I am and you can't sit here all night. That would worry me, really it would.

'Please Carol, for me, go and phone Alan, get your lift and get back to the horses. Keep an eye on them eh? That's a good girl.'

Wearied by his long speech, he closed his eyes, and sank deeply into his pillow.

When I returned from the phone, the curtains were drawn closed and when they opened a staff nurse wheeled out a small trolley. 'He's ready now, Mrs Smith. Had his prep and pre-med.'

'Is he asleep?' I asked.

'Not quite. When is your lift due? Half-an-hour or so? Well, he should be just about on his way to theatre then. Phone us later tonight for a progress report.' She smiled warmly and went about her duties.

Unlike the rest of the day which had dragged on in agonizingly slow motion, the thirty minutes I spent quietly sitting by his bedside somehow just evaporated. As the clock hands moved relentlessly towards six o'clock, I knew I would have to leave him to meet my lift outside the main door. At least, I reassured myself, he is peaceful at the moment. At least he's free from pain. I moved my chair back against the wall as quietly as I could. I stood to take my leave, bending over to gently kiss him goodbye. As my lips brushed his cheek he stirred and murmured 'Why? Oh God, why?' And those words echoed round and round in my head as I sat on the steps outside the hospital weeping, uncaring of the concerned or embarrassed stares of passers-by. Weeping to try and empty my heart and mind of all feeling, of every emotion, of all memory. Why? Dear God, why?

The concern and support of the carriage driving fraternity was waiting like the embrace of a close family on my return to Lowther. Everything was organized, everything attended to. It had even been arranged that Ray Brown would drive the cobs in the cones the next morning so that the assembled Montan guests would at least have a glimpse of the horses.

It was a 9.30 pm call that finally informed me that surgery was complete, the pins in place, and Richard safely back in bed in his ward and – in that most maddening of meaningless hospital jargon – 'quite satisfactory'. There was nothing left to do with the rest of the night but get it over with.

I awoke from a nightmare of horses and mangled legs, with my expired hot-water bottle lying comfortless beside me. I dressed quickly to escape from the awful solitude of the trailer and stepped out into the embrace of the Lakeland hills. The girls had performed the only tribute they could to Richard; that morning the horses looked as beautiful, as well-groomed as if they were about to enter some important competition. Their coats gleamed, their hooves shone and the brass on their harness winked in the sunlight. Our turnout was immaculate and, even under Ray's totally unfamiliar guidance, Bear and Blizzard trotted into that arena as composed and as settled as if he'd been driving them every day for years. As soon as they left the arena I stripped out of my livery and made a dash for the hospital, bracing myself to face I did not know what.

It was, to my astonishment and relief, a very cheerful-looking Richard that smiled at me from the end bed where I'd left him so still and drawn the night before. A cage covered with a light cotton sheet was over his right leg. 'My word, you look . . . well much better than I'd hoped!'

'I don't feel too bad at all; I wasn't so good earlier this morning though.'

The next and unavoidable question had to be 'How is your leg?' The white tent that was draped over his leg kept it discreetly out of view.

'How is your stomach?' Richard quipped lightly in retaliation.

I paled, 'Is it really as bad as that?'

'Let's put it this way, I found it very – disturbing – to look at at first, but honestly, I promise you, it doesn't feel the way it looks. And if I've got to get used to it I expect you will have to as well.'

'Is it – gory?' I whispered: blood, in its liquid, red state was the one sight guaranteed to render me flat on my back in a very short space of time.

'Oh no,' said Richard positively, 'it's not gory at all – just a bit gruesome.'

I was about to protest that surely 'gory' and 'gruesome' were one and the same thing, when he folded back the sheet.

I was suitably disturbed.

Admittedly, he had been right when he said the leg was not gory. There was not a trace of blood anywhere. The lower middle part of the leg where the jagged bones had torn through the flesh showed only a line of neat black stitches in bruise-blackened skin, still liberally daubed with bright yellow antiseptic. It was the leg above and below the stitched area that took the eye, the brain and, yes, the stomach some adjusting to. Four, long, bright stainless steel pins, two above and two below, simply disappeared through neat round holes into his leg. Attached to these pins and lying parallel to his leg was a device that was about a foot long, grey metal, and looked for all the world like a hydraulic suspension unit from a motor bike. 'My God!' was all I could manage to utter.

'It's quite impressive actually,' Richard said lightly. 'It's called a Fixator. It will act like an exterior bone, taking the body weight and allowing . . .'

'Yes, yes,' I interrupted his flow, 'they did try and explain all that last night. It's just the reality of it is slightly different to the theory.' I gazed appalled and yet fascinated by the sight before my eyes.

'Apparently, where the threads of the pins go into the leg has to be cleaned every day to prevent infection. That's the only bit I'm not looking forward to.'

In my heart I wondered if that would prove to be the only unpleasantness that the future held before that shattered limb was whole and normal again, but I held my counsel. The rest of the visit passed the way hospital visits do – in handing over cards and presents, writing lists of things to be taken in and exchanging small-talk.

I called at the Sister's office on my way out to thank the staff for their care and kindness and for allowing me to visit out of visiting hours. And to raise the previously unasked question: 'How long?' The answer nearly required my own admission to a hospital bed.

It was obviously a very severe break, the Sister emphasized, and so, well, the best we could expect was two to three weeks at Carlisle. And then? And then – well that was more difficult. The pins could come out in, maybe three to four months; it could be six months until it was properly healed – but I wasn't to hold her to that: strange, obstinate things, bones. Her estimates were on the optimistic side. I asked her whether Richard had been told this yet?

He hadn't asked – when he did, he would be told.

Back at Lowther, I had to hang on to doing what I was best at: being practical. The horsebox and trailer, with their cargo of horse and carriages, had to be loaded for the journey home. Willing volunteers made the task easy and with Ray Brown driving the horsebox and myself bringing up the rear with car and caravan our sad little convoy left Lowther and headed for home. I drove back sobered and frightened by what the coming months could hold, my world once more shattered as surely as Richard's leg.

I arrived expecting a house that was cold, chaotic and unwelcoming. I found, to my grateful delight, the kitchen stove singing with the promise of gallons of piping hot bath water, delicious savoury smells issuing from the oven and a pan of neatly peeled potatoes sitting waiting to boil. A note from my indefatigable friend Brenda Hamson identified her as the thoughtful organizer and provider for my bodily comforts. There could have been, I thought, as I gratefully ladled delicious casserole on to plates for myself and the girls, no truer or more welcome display of friendship possible than this meal.

After the girls had retired to their own room for the evening, the weariness of the ordeal began to take its toll on me again, but it was a long, long time before I could escape to bed because the phone literally never stopped ringing. Close friends, acquaintances, officials from the driving world, all enquiring, all anxious, all caring. How kind, I thought, as I crawled drained and exhausted into bed, how very, very kind everyone had been to me, to Richard, to both of us.

With the morning came more fears and more tears. How to cope alone? What would become of the horses? What would happen to our hope of new sponsorship?

Two kind enquirers did help me put our problems into perspective a little, however; one was a card that arrived from a young lad I knew simply as 'David'. He adored the carriage driving world and was a familiar face at many events. The card was in braille – David was blind. The second was a phone call from a very distraught Heather Stoddart who had somehow received the news on the grapevine. She pointed out with genuine relief and not a single trace of self-pity that the accident could have been much, much worse.

My next visit to the hospital, with Megan, was to a Richard whose face clearly showed that the last couple of days had been far from pleasant. The crutches at the end of the bed told their own story.

He was now required to get up several times a day and go a few steps along the ward. The resultant rush of blood to his injured leg was, he informed me in language moderated for Megan's sake, pure agony, and his foot would subsequently swell up like a red suet pudding and he had to have large icepacks put on it. The physiotherapist had also started her own specialized line in torture on him and Richard paled visibly on simply mentioning her name. It was not a happy visit.

Megan was able to cope with the reality of Richard's alien-looking leg far better than many of the adults. In fact she was totally fascinated by it, but the quiet yet not quite private huddles around each bed soon became boring and restrictive for her once the news and small talk had been exchanged. I escaped, guiltily but thankfully, to take her home as soon as I possibly could.

A few nights later Ray Brown and Alan Robson arrived with a plan. There was month to go before the National Championships, the event at which Alan had hoped to clinch a new deal for us: an enjoyable day out with the ancient ramparts of Windsor Castle in the background and plenty of 'corporate hospitality' would work wonders in that department, Alan was sure, regardless of what the horses did or did not achieve. But it was essential that they were *there* and did at least compete, otherwise the central theme was lost. All we were short of to continue with this carefully organized plan, Alan tactfully pointed out, was a driver. That, of course, was where Ray Brown came in. He was qualified in his own right to drive at the Nationals, and permission had been sought from and gladly given by the powers that be for him to drive our horses.

'And Richard?' I asked in a small voice.

'A month is a very long time away,' Alan reassured me. 'He's bound to be home by then, and much improved. Most probably he could even come if we took the caravan for him to sleep in and he was managing his crutches all right. We could even get a wheelchair for him so he could get round in comfort. And if, for some reason, he isn't allowed to go, I'm sure he would be the first to insist that the horses did. After all,' Alan continued bluntly, 'it's the only chance they have at the moment, isn't it?'

It was only after they'd gone, leaving me much heartened, that the irony hit me.

The wheel of fate had come round full circle. It had taken six years, but it had finally come round: the national Championships at Windsor – on crutches and with a wheelchair. Only six years ago it had been *me* who had hobbled painfully but proudly around to watch Bear, driven single by Richard, making his attempt on the title. I remembered clearly the promise that if I 'behaved myself' in hospital I would be allowed to go was the only carrot that had kept me going through the long, testing days and weeks. Well, perhaps the next day when I visited Richard I would be able to dangle that same carrot before his despairing eyes and bring the light of hope and determination back into them. I had a much better night's sleep.

The next morning a somewhat bewildered Helen was informed she had to resume a full training schedule and keep the horses fit for the National Championships at Windsor the following month.

It seemed that I had just got into a sort of routine when a

delighted Richard greeted me with news which, whilst it pleased me, also alarmed me in its implications. He could come home. He could manage his crutches, manage cleaning his pins, and it was important that he moved around as much as possible. The doctor had also told him that, provided there were no set-backs, he could go to Windsor. I was unsure as to which prospect pleased him the most.

I argued long and hard to persuade him to have a bed brought downstairs: it would be so very much easier for him I insisted, with our almost vertical open staircase. But no, emphatically *no*. He was coming *home* to his own house and his own bed – in his own bedroom.

Clothing him suitably then became my next priority. There was no way he could pull a pair of trousers over his 'fixated' leg. A couple of track suit bottoms with the inside leg stitching unpicked to the knee and replaced with velcro provided a perfect solution. The leg looked perfectly normal – apart from four metal pins sticking out through his trousers. Anxious that they should not suffer the slightest knock the nurses diligently fitted the ends with eye-catching bright red plastic knobs.

A similar anxiety on my part accounted for Richard's somewhat unorthodox transport home. I was terrified at the thought of squeezing Richard – legs, crutches, pins, knobs and all – through a car door. Thus it was he travelled home resplendent on a large bean bag cushion in the back of Brenda's estate car.

The adrenalin produced by the sheer joy of getting home after a long and, for Richard, unexpected and traumatic, hospital stay is a marvellous thing. But it can only sustain you for so long.

By early evening Richard was showing clear signs of being exhausted, in pain, and in need of bed. The journey up our stairs was as anguished and arduous as a Himalayan ascent. I was terrified he would slip or fall. The gradient was gruelling and every hop upwards sent shock waves through both his legs. I remembered quite vividly how I had simply given out on my way upstairs on my crutches at the cottage and how Richard had had to gather me in his arms and carry me the rest of the way. There was no way I could possibly do him the same service. All I could do was encourage and steady him. I could have admonished him over his stubbornness about not having a bed downstairs, but then I remembered wryly that I had refused to have one either.

Slowly, we inched our way up until there was one step to go. The top one.

Of course, being the house that Richard Smith built and thus not having two doors that matched, nor a true 90 degree angle in the place, we should have remembered that the top step was, for some reason, two inches higher than the rest of the flight.

As he made his last exhausted hop up, the bottom two pins in his leg just grazed the top of the tread. He cried out like a startled child, more in fright than in pain, and collapsed down on the landing. There, for the first time since the accident, the tears welled and flowed freely and great racking sobs shook his body. 'I'm useless! Bloody useless! Oh what am I going to do!' was all he could wrench out, over and over.

And I could only repeat with a certainty I was far from feeling, 'It'll be all right, you'll see, it'll be all right.'

We did get into a routine of sorts reasonably well. So anxious was Richard to get to Windsor, which was only a couple of weeks away, that he subjected himself with amazing tolerance to the nasty necessities of the day. Thus, he actually allowed me to do his physiotherapy exercises, which he hated and were agony, with him. He observed all the fanatically strict hygiene rules surrounding the cleaning of the flesh around the pins in his leg: another horrific ordeal. He allowed me to assist him in and out of the bath from a stool with his damaged leg encased in a heavy duty polythene bag and elevated out of the water. He didn't flinch from the district nurse on her regular visits to poke and prod and peer, and he didn't even put up much resistance when I had a wheelchair delivered with an elevated leg rest for him to use at Windsor.

And, lo and behold, the second week in September, some five weeks after his accident, saw our familiar procession heading south. Only this time there was the unfamiliar Brown family caravan bobbing along behind us, and the *very* unfamiliar presence of Richard sitting beside me in the passenger seat of the car instead of ahead of me driving the horsebox.

It was not the best National Championship we had competed at, but then it was far from the worst. In fact after the marathon, Raymond was lying fourth in the competition, a fantastic achievement for a man who had never driven the horses across country before. Dashing from hazard to hazard across country with Richard in his wheelchair, waving his crutches in his excitement and his effort to urge me on still faster, was my own particular phenomenal achievement of that competition. Sadly, Raymond had a poor cones round which knocked him down to sixth place, but it was still a remarkable achievement. Our important company guests came and saw and went, and the word from Alan was that they were quite taken with the 'carriage driving thing': it was very novel and exciting and there would be 'no problems' over next season, they reassured us. Other than getting Richard's leg better, of course.

Once the last horse had been put in the wagon and the ramp closed with great finality – and, for my part, enormous relief – on the season of 1988, we headed off on the long journey north to try and do just that.

11

Grasp the Nettle

I returned to Bishop Auckland College straight after the Nationals to discover that, along with a stunned Sandee Pattison, I actually had no job to return to.

Enrolment had been disastrous. Many courses were not running and part-time staff just weren't needed.

Being a part-timer at a college is always an insecure state of affairs. I knew very well that employment was on a week-to-week basis and entirely dependent upon student numbers. However, now into my third year at the college, the job had taken on a degree of permanence for me. More alarmingly, my job represented the only real financial security that we had.

Montan were being incredibly supportive and as generous as was possible, and I knew we had six months on full pay, but Richard was well into the second month of that already and the healing process had hardly begun. What would happen if by January he wasn't fully fit again? How long could we manage on DSS handouts before our world crashed round our ears? The reality of our predicament finally hit home – and hard. There was nothing for it, I would have to find a full-time job.

My new-found sense of direction took a dizzying blow when one morning I took Megan out to her school bus and was confronted with the mutilated, lifeless form of Pansy, my lovely little calico cat, smeared across the road in front of the house. I wept bitter, angry tears that she should be lost so senselessly. Senseless loss: that seemed to be the theme of our lives at that time and I seemed only to be able to rage helplessly against it. Dark thoughts even lurked in my heart about Richard. They say that God gives to each person one special gift, one special talent. For the first time ever I mused rather bitterly over why Richard had been given the ability to drive horses. It was the one talent he had that marked him apart from most other mortals. But now, with his leg smashed, the sponsorship up in the air and my job gone, how I wished, how I prayed, his gift had been in book-keeping or even as a successful milkman.

Having determined that a full-time job was what was required did not mean that one was going to be easily acquired. I decided that, as an emergency measure, I would have to try and pick up supply work in schools or colleges where, through unforeseen absences, vacancies or additional work they were anxious to get cover at the start of the educational year.

Remembering that I'd got my teaching hours at Bishop Auckland through a recommendation by Sandee, I wondered if a 'who you knew' approach might be more successful than a 'cold sell'. So, putting behind me the disappointment of having to leave Bishop Tec, I phoned up one of the lecturers I'd worked with there.

'I've got two leads you could follow up,' Pauline Candlish suggested. 'Both colleges I've done part-time work for in the past. Can't promise they'll be able to help, but they might be better off with hours than we are here at Bishop. One is Darlington College of Technology. Then there's Peterlee College – The School of Special Needs; I've worked there, too, and they're often looking for part-timers.'

'Peterlee!' I squeaked. 'That's miles away; it's on the coast, isn't it?'

'Well, strangely enough, I bet from where you live it's

not much further away than Darlington, probably about ten miles from Durham City. I take it you're not averse to travelling reasonable distances?'

'Pauline,' I assured her, 'I'd travel anywhere I could get to in a day and back to get work at present.'

Then another thought struck me. 'What do you mean by School of Special Needs?'

'Well, exactly that – kids with special educational needs. Some are disabled, physically or mentally, some both. Then there are kids who have learning difficulties or emotional problems or social problems – or all of them!' she laughed at the other end of the phone.

'Disabled kids! Problem kids! I don't think I have the experience to cope with that.'

Pauline laughed again. 'That's what I thought when I started there. Right in at the deep end I was. But I discovered there are only two real requirements for coping with those kids.'

'And those are?' I enquired nervously.

'A lot of patience and a sense of humour; and I know you've got both of those! You'd probably love it there. Shall I give my friend Diane there a ring and see if there's anything going? You did say *any* work, *any* where, didn't you?'

'Well, yes I did,' I had to admit. 'And Pauline, thanks very much.'

Following these leads I scraped together about two-thirds of my permitted part-time lecturing hours in my first week of effort. My schedule was going to be peculiar and some days the travelling murderous: one day a week I was at Peterlee *and* Darlington which totted up to a round trip of over seventy miles. Luckily my Mini was wonderfully frugal on its petrol consumption.

All my fears of working with Special Needs proved unfounded. My first experience was with a group of lovely people from the local Adult Training Centre who came to college for a literacy class. Their lesson allowed me to adjust my perspective to the philosophy, tempo and demands of the department in general. Appetite whetted, when the opportunity was offered to work with a group of full-time students on a life skills programme, I took it with interest and enthusiasm – as well as gratitude. Gradually, as the term progressed, so did my hours with Special Needs until, apart from my twice weekly dash to Darlington, they represented the bulk of my teaching.

Richard thought he was making progress when they took his Fixator out of his leg and replaced it with a plaster cast. He was wrong: he found himself about half a mile behind the starting post. Whereas with his Fixator on he'd been able to get into a comfortable sleeping position, with the plaster on, he could not. Whereas he'd been mobile and independent because he had been able to drive the car and walk (albeit with crutches) with his foot on the ground, with the plaster on, he could not. His days had become surprisingly pain-free with his Fixator on and he required few pain-killing tablets. With the pot on, he was watching the clock to see how soon he could take the next ones. Whereas he had, most of the time, become hopeful and even cheerful about the whole situation, convinced that things were progressing well, after only a few weeks hobbling round, non-weight-bearing on crutches, unable to snatch more than a few hours' sleep and trapped and isolated at home all day while I was at work, he became desperate. He looked desperate; his face drawn and nipped into pain lines. He was certainly desperate to live with, fluctuating between despair, anger and irritability.

The door of the year was creaking ever slowly towards its close; we were by now into December. Surely, I told myself, nothing further unpleasant could squeeze itself into our lives in the time that was left?

No sooner had I thought the thought than a phone call from a devastated Alan Robson told us that everything had gone horrendously wrong within the newly merged Montan Group. The receiver had stepped in and everything was frozen. What was immediately clear was that there was no question of any money for frills such as horses, nor indeed could the smaller, weaker company subsidiaries survive.

Montan Transport was being wound up. Richard had lost both his sponsorship and his job.

We were both literally too numb to talk about it – and anyway, what was there to discuss, this was the end of the line. What a grand finale to a year of frustration, misfortune and sorrow.

In the space of four months Richard had had his accident, lost his sponsorship and lost his job. It certainly totted up to Great-aunt Meg's favourite curse about bad luck coming in threes.

Richard, defeated by the day, had hauled his weary body and lead-weight leg painfully up the stairs to bed and a couple of tablets. I knew I simply wouldn't, couldn't, sleep and had sought refuge in the lounge feeling cynical and bitter.

In front of the unconvincing warmth of a one-bar electric fire, like Ebenezer Scrooge, I had a visitation of Christmas Past. When I had been married to Megan's father the festive season had been an altogether more opulent affair. None of your Gateway Special Ruby then, nor a quarter wedge of polythene-wrapped St Michael's Stilton, grossly under-ripe. The real things had groaned on the sideboard; the cheese festering in its dish until it was nearly liquid and vying with the port for its vintage and crustiness. How abundant life had been then I reflected, how wonderfully abundant. The six-course Christmas dinner, the obligatory brace of pheasants, the blazing log fires. The Boxing Day meet of hounds to shake it all down and give one an appetite for the next night's gluttony. I would be lying if I pretended I didn't miss it. I would frequently wander my five-bedroom farmhouse in my dreams and check the antiques, admire the hunting prints, caress my Aga. On a more practical level I missed being able to fill the car with petrol on the account whenever I wanted. It had been the good life, my friends would remind me, still bewildered at my decision to leave it all behind. But ill-health and bad luck had destroyed the true inner warmth behind those logs blazing so merrily in the grate and now I was ... I was out on my own. 'Grasp the Nettle' was my motto, but I wasn't altogether sure that the sting of this one might not be fatal. But I knew what had to be done. And soon.

It was no use pretending life could go on as it had for the last three years; the truth had to be faced. Richard wasn't even able to walk, let alone drive for the foreseeable future. Now he was also without a job and we had lost our sponsors for the horses. Even dismissing poor Helen and it being the middle of our close season didn't stop the bills coming in. For shoes, for vets, for bedding, for hay – a part-time lecturer's job wasn't going to foot the bills. I would definitely have to go and see the bank manager as soon as possible.

All things conspired to bring me down. Working a long, hard day with a long, hard drive at each end; having to run a home with all the shopping, fetching and carrying because Richard was still out of action. The way I was beginning to feel it would have taken a very big Pools win to really cheer me up.

All around me the orgy of Christmas spending seemed to be reaching a climax: the shops groaned with goods and luring offers of credit – Free! Now! – for those whose consciences or purse-strings were tight. On my weekly trudge around the supermarket it became harder and

harder to resist dropping an extra bit of this, a small bottle
of that into the trolley.

'. . . Tis the season to be jolly!' the tinny speakers tinkled
out as I grimly steered away from someone whose trolley
was so overflowing with bottles he looked like a mobile
off-licence. Jolly indeed!

'. . . Troll the ancient yuletide carol!' Now that was more
like it – I felt exactly that: the original Ancient Yuletide
Carol. Just to complete my festive season, it would be my
birthday in ten days' time; my thirty-ninth. The beginning
of my fortieth year. It was rarely the best of dates to have
a birthday in the best of years, but this year for the first
time I truly hoped the day would just pass unnoticed,
eclipsed by the stern almost war-time conditions into
which our lives seemed to have been plunged.

Almost to spite myself I threw a couple of packs of cheap
Christmas cards into the trolley at the check-out.

'. . . Tra la la lah, la lah lah lah!' the taped music ground
relentlessly on. 'And the same to you!' I wished it.

The days galloped on towards Christmas. I tried to
ignore it all; like Scrooge, I tried to view it through hum-
bug-tinted glasses. But somehow the ancient annual magic
seeped in through the chinks in my armour. First the tea-
towel and dressing-gown brigade at Megan's school,
clutching their tinsel halos and cuddling their toys,
watching wide-eyed as a six-year-old Mary, resplendent in
a blue curtain, reverently placed her baby in a straw-filled
dolly's cot. And then, the next night, before my defences
had time to regroup, the Brownie carol service.

'Hush you my baby the night wind is cold.
The lambs from the hillside are safe in the fold,
Sleep with the midnight and wake with the morn,
For the Lord of all glory, a baby, is born.'

Megan enunciated carefully in her Speech and Drama

Grade II voice in her grand solo slot of the evening. And deep inside me something very precious tingled and flowed. Faith? Well, at least hope then? Pah! Sentimental humbug!

As with Tiny Tim, it was the littlest one that finally broke through my Scrooge-like blanket of apathy. The most diminutive Brownie I have ever seen, reaching barely past the belt of her neighbouring Pixie, her brown tights wrinkled on her sparrow-like legs, so small that all that was visible above her hymn sheet was the pom-pom on the top of her brown woolly hat, lifted her clear little voice and rendered her solo offering:

'Bless all the dear children in Thy tender care,
And fit us for heaven to live with Thee there.'

A fat, warm tear trickled, despite all my efforts, down my cheek and landed squarely on my mince pie.

She was, this tiny ray of light, unbelievably named Holly and, as the newest Brownie, Brown Owl asked her to draw the raffle tickets.

'591!' Brown Owl announced. Megan gave a squeal of delight and rushed forward, nearly upending the entire back bench full of bigger Brownies.

And so, clutching my unexpected bottle of Rosé Lambrusco ('I thought you'd like the wine Mummy: I didn't take the chocolates!') I finally capitulated, launched into another mince pie and the final rousing chorus of the evening.

'. . . we wish you a Merry Christmas,
And a Happy New Year!'

This particular Ancient Yuletide Carol was definitely warmed by the Christmas spirit. Rallied, I faced my appointment with the bank manager.

*

I arrived at the bank with heart and feet like lead. For once, I had no persuasive tactics up my sleeve, no carefully worked out arguments to get us a little more on the overdraft. I had nothing but the truth to tell and it would in some ways be a blessed relief, an excuse to finally step off the treadmill of trying to keep our wheels going round. And so I told Mr Graham about Richard's painfully slow progress with his leg, about his having no job, about us having no sponsors. Had he said 'Mrs Smith, I think perhaps we have come to the end of the road this time,' I would have heartily and completely agreed with him. The only thing I did ask him for was a little time before the books were closed: time for Richard to adjust and accept in his own heart that he couldn't hope to compete again. In his current state of mind, if all hope was taken away, however forlorn and unrealistic, then Richard's world would finally collapse and he could be swept away with it. I asked for three months' grace to the spring sales, so that the horses could be sold at their true value. If I could gain that one small concession I had steeled myself to accept whatever hard line he might take over our future. But I had got it all wrong.

Mr Graham listened very carefully to all I had to say, looked at the prices I thought the horses, the carriages and harness would fetch and read the letter dissolving our sponsorship with Montan.

In my preparations for reacting to his response, I had failed utterly. How did we know what time factor was involved in Richard's leg healing? he asked. Surely the horses were essential and irreplaceable if we were to compete in a serious manner ever again? Had we ever seriously thought about other avenues of sponsorship? Richard's leg mightn't be healed for him to compete at the *start* of next season, but surely a lot could happen before the *end* of the season? If we didn't manage to compete in the coming year, then surely the cost of just keeping the horses ticking

over wouldn't be so great? Of course if in twelve months'
time there was no hope of Richard's leg mending sufficiently, or no sponsor on the horizon, we would have to
seriously consider selling up next year. But for now – well
it would be short-sighted; it would be illogical.

A year? He was giving us twelve months! I sat too numb
with disbelief to move. For one of the few times in my life,
I was at a total loss for words, for Mr Graham's Christmas
gift went beyond faith in us, it provided us with more than
vague hope. His gift was that most priceless of things –
time. He was allowing us to buy *time*.

I'd heard of the expression 'walking on air'. I'd always
associated it with rather slushy romantic songs, with a
state of over-excited euphoria. But I wasn't excited when I
came out of the bank, if anything I was unnaturally calm
and totally composed. So composed I had to keep checking
I was actually breathing and that I was actually heading
in the right direction, because for some unknown reason I
was getting very little impression of contact with the
ground through the soles of my feet. Bishop Auckland
High Street had never looked so beautiful. The Salvation
Army band playing on the corner crystallized my
emotions: '. . . the hopes and fears of all the years are met
in Thee tonight.'

I bought a large bunch of mistletoe and a bottle of sherry
– decent sherry – and headed for home.

Brandishing the mistletoe in one hand and a tray of
glasses in the other, I kissed each astounded girl on the
yard in turn, saving a totally astonished Richard till last.

He eyed me suspiciously. 'You're either tiddly or else
you've robbed the bank.'

'Neither: I am stone cold sober – though I could be tiddly
within the hour and the bank doesn't need robbing because
it will let us have enough money to keep the horses going
till we find out more clearly where we *are* going. And
there's no hurry Richard, no panic any more!'

I was getting slightly hysterical with sheer relief. Well, relief and sherry – a heady mixture. 'Don't you see? You don't have to kill yourself to get driving again for this spring – he's given us a whole year, a whole, beautiful year!'

Richard sipped his sherry very thoughtfully and very quietly. 'A year to drive again eh?'

'I thought you'd be pleased – well, thrilled actually,' I said, disappointment creeping round the edges of my voice.

'Oh I am pleased, I'm delighted: it's just such a surprise, it's almost a shock.'

'Yes I know,' I admitted reluctantly. 'That's exactly how I felt when I came out of the bank, but now, well now it's beginning to sink in! Oh I know it's not the answer to everything: we've still got to work out how we're going to live now your job has gone. But it's a lifeline, Richard, a lifeline for the horses!'

'Look, Carol, my leg's giving me a bit of stick and I need some pain-killers, but my tummy's very empty and pills are no good on an empty tummy. Could you make a sandwich or two – may as well make lunch for the girls while you're at it – and just bring mine out here on the yard, eh? I want to get on as best I can while this mild weather holds. Good lass.' And with this dismissal he turned back to his welding.

Slightly crestfallen I returned to the house and began buttering bread and slicing tomatoes and grating cheese. I hadn't expected Richard to swoon at my feet with delight, but I had expected . . . well, a reaction . . . a hug and a kiss, a pat on the head for my nettle-grasping.

But I had underestimated him; the truly unexpected awaited me on the yard when I took the plate of sandwiches out. There on top of the carriage in the middle of the yard, looking only vaguely apprehensive, sat Richard and waiting at the end of the reins for the command to move off stood Bear and Blizzard, the girls at their heads.

'What . . .' I gasped.

Richard patted the cushion beside him, 'Can't offer you sleigh bells and snow Mrs Smith,' he said, 'but I can offer you a Christmas ride with your staggeringly talented and good-looking horses.'

'Richard . . . you shouldn't be up there . . . your leg! I don't think . . .'

'Coming or not?' he said with great finality, gathering up his reins and whip.

'Coming!' I yelled, depositing tray, sandwiches and coffee on the lawn and climbing up and over the back of the carriage to sit in my long-accustomed position.

The last time he had sat in any carriage had been on 6 August, four-and-a-half-months before at Lowther.

'All right girls, stand back!' he said to the groom. 'Walk on, Boys, walk on!'

It wasn't the longest drive in my life, it wasn't the most exciting, but it was one of the most important, the most memorable and the very best Christmas present Richard could have given me. We didn't go far and I could see when we bounced and bumped up the back lane at a fast trot that the bumping was reverberating up his leg which he had carefully braced and padded. But on his face, through the discomfort, there was, shining out, determination, real hope and new life.

'Whoa, bonny lads!' he said as he pulled up into the yard and handed me the reins.

The horses had been as exhilarated by their unexpected trip out as Richard: they had not been driven since Windsor, three months previously, and not by Richard since Lowther. No toddle around the block for them; they had pulled and pranced and snorted as if they were on peak form.

Very carefully and very ungracefully Richard slid out of

his seat and out of the carriage. Jo was there with his crutches before he hit the ground.

'A year indeed!' Richard muttered as he headed back towards his workshop. 'I don't need any year to drive my horses. By God; just watch me, just let them all watch me!'

On New Year's Eve, with Richard long since in bed, I listened to Big Ben on the radio, drank a small glass of sherry and then gathered together the traditional items with which my father had always 'first footed' our home: a piece of coal, a piece of food and a coin. This year, I was determined, the omens and fates would be placated from day one.

I opened the back door and slipped out into the clear, dark night. Like a flash, a small shape darted out after me, took one sniff of the chill air and shot back into the house. My Christmas present from Richard and Megan, in what had been the most frugal of Christmases, had come in the shape of a frail, pathetic tortoiseshell kitten, rescued from the animal sanctuary to fill the void caused by Pansy's death. I had christened her 'Holly' and had doubted whether she would survive till Boxing Day. Now, after only one week of injections, good food and being spoilt rotten, she was a bundle of curious, affectionate energy – and trying to upstage my first-footing rituals.

Ah well I thought, she is *nearly* black and she is certainly one lucky little cat as she shouldn't even be alive now. Perhaps she is a good omen for the house. But nevertheless, as I re-entered the kitchen and placed my ritual offerings on the table, I whispered with great earnestness, 'May food and warmth and money be never lacking from this home. May love and health and peace be with us all this year.'

I closed the door firmly on 1988.

A New Year had begun.

12

Back in Harness

The year had hardly turned its corner before I had one important stroke of luck. Peterlee College offered me a whole term's full-time employment in the School of Special Needs because a member of staff was on secondment. It was only until Easter, of course, but in the cold, dark days of early January Easter felt a long way off.

Loss of independence and loss of income left Richard frustrated and dissatisfied, even at times bitter and resentful. He tried to work in his workshop, clumping around clumsily with his pot on his leg, welder in one hand, crutch in the other, but it often made him even more frustrated. He was finding it particularly hard to accept that I was now the family bread-winner and that he had no income whatsoever. All he could do was to stomp impotently around the yard by day and toss restlessly and pain-racked in bed at night. His regular trips to the hospital were not encouraging and when by mid-February the bones were showing no signs of uniting, a very drastic course of action was decided upon.

It sounded quite logical when you said it quickly: basically, they were going to lift off Richard's kneecap. Then they were going to insert a stainless steel rod down through the shin bone and 'thread' all the broken pieces of bone on to it. Rather like a kebab skewer. Then they were going to bolt the bottom of the rod through his ankle, to prevent it slipping back up through the leg. And then, of course, they would replace his kneecap. This rod would stay in place for a year, and then the operation would have to be reversed.

It was when you said it slowly and *thought* about it that the hair stood up on the back of your neck.

I delivered him to the hospital in Sunderland where the operation was to be performed and returned to work at Peterlee. I can't pretend my mind was honestly on my job that day. One thing I had discovered early about my 'special' students was that they could be alarmingly honest and they expected the same courtesy in return. Comments like 'Er – you don't look nice in that dress!' or 'What have you done to your hair?' would be commonplace, though it was the ones like 'You look bonny today Mrs Smith!' or 'You're my friend' that lodged themselves more firmly in my memory banks.

That Tuesday the repeated questions were 'What's the matter Mrs Smith?' and 'Eee, Mrs Smith, have you been crying?' So I told them my husband was having an operation on his leg that day and I was very worried about him. By the time I left college for the hospital I had a sheaf of 'Get Well Mr Smith' cards under my arm. Unknown senders to an unknown recipient – but with wishes that were filled with total sincerity.

When I arrived at the hospital that evening, Richard was far from recovered from his anaesthetic. I was shocked by what I saw as he lay moving his head restlessly and making a noise that was between a groan and a whimper. His hands spouted drip tubes, and from his elevated leg a drain tube channelled a trickle of dark red, sticky blood into a collecting bag on the side of the bed. The elastic that held an oxygen mask in place was cutting cruelly into the back of one ear and his tongue moved hopelessly over the parched, cracked lips of one newly returned from surgery.

I sank on to a chair by the bed quite sickened. He mumbled a few times and flickered in and out of consciousness, but I don't think he knew I was there. What torture was he being subjected to now? What if, after all this, the leg was no better? Or even worse? Dear God, was this nightmare never, ever going to end.

I gave way to tears then, sat there by the bedside, crying silently into the little towel I had hung on his locker that morning, my knee bumping against the plastic bag of dark, warm blood.

It was a long and unhappy drive home, and once Megan was in bed I simply sat, numbed, in front of the kitchen stove with the light out. Not even Holly's little rumbling engine of a body on my lap could comfort me.

The next day, my students informed me that I looked 'Really awful, Mrs Smith' and they were deadly accurate, as usual. I drove from work to Sunderland with even more trepidation than the night before. What pain-racked, crippled vision would greet me this time?

'I hope you've brought me something to eat – I'm absolutely starving!' said Richard cheerfully from his bed as soon as I entered.

I blinked hard. This surely wasn't the same man I'd seen only twenty-four hours before. More shocks were in store. He'd been up out of bed. He had *walked* the length of the ward on crutches. The physiotherapist was a retired Gestapo officer, he confided.

On the following night, he informed me he had walked to the bathroom several times that day and, biggest shock of all, I could collect him after work the next night and take him *home*.

They say modern medicine is a miracle: I say they are right. On the Monday morning I had delivered to that hospital a hopeless man, burdened with a heavy plaster cast, unable to put his foot to the floor without pain and struggling to walk even with crutches. On the Friday night

I took home a man renewed; a man who could walk quite freely, with only a walking stick, and from whose face the lines of constant pain were already fading.

There were still problems, of course, not least that I would be unemployed again in a few weeks and we would have no income whatsoever. Sandee Pattison, having turned her back on the teaching profession and settled happily with an agency doing charity work for people with social problems, promised me she would keep her 'ear to the ground'.

Employment was a problem I was pushing to the back of my mind in my delight at Richard's progress. Able to walk almost without a limp, though with the aid of a stick, he set himself to tackle everything that had been impossible for him over the last six months. Horses were driven regularly. A new battle-wagon arose from an unlikely assortment of bits of metal on the floor of his workshop. Most mysteriously, for me anyway, he arrived home one day with the decaying remains of a large caravan chassis.

'What on earth's that for?' I enquired dubiously, seeing only a few metal girders astride an axle.

' "That", as you call it, is your new home.'

'Pardon?'

'Your dream home; what you've always wanted.'

'*Pardon*?' I could still only see a few lumps of scrap metal.

'You have complained on and off for the last four years about the inadequacies of the trailer as a summer home.'

'Yes, well . . . it is a bit like a sardine tin on wet or dull days when the door is closed with only that one little window at the front. And it would be so nice to have somewhere comfy to sit of an evening instead of just on the edge of the bed – particularly somewhere to sit with a view. And better still if the roof didn't leak over the bed when it rains hard . . . but I'm not really *complaining*!' I added hastily, remembering with horror the days of eking out our existence in the bowels of the horsebox or, even worse, in a cold, wet tent on the ground.

'You're quite right: it's totally inadequate as a place to live – mainly because it was never purpose-built as a trailer to live in, simply as a trailer to carry carts about in. This new model will have it all!'

'All?' I enquired cautiously. One learnt to be cautious after seven years of life with Richard.

'Kitchen units, comfy seating, panoramic view, a new cooker: even a bedroom!'

'Bedroom!'

'Well, bed-shelf, actually,' Richard conceded.

'Shelf?' I was switching to maximum suspiciousness now.

'This trailer will be much higher than the old one; high enough to put in a "mezzanine" level over the table and seating arrangements at the front. It means we can have the bed out of the way, as it can be left made up and in place between shows, not like the old one where everything had to be tied up against the wall.'

'How do we get up to this bed – upper level – shelf – whatever?' I was asking the most stupid and most obvious questions now because they were usually the ones that, in his enthusiasm, Richard hadn't thought about.

'Anything wrong with a stepladder?' he retaliated, equally obviously.

'But your leg; how are you going to climb up ladders safely?'

'I'm sure it won't be any more difficult than climbing up on the cart, and I'm managing that splendidly.'

'What's to stop us just rolling off this – shelf?' was my final, it's-obvious-you-idiot question.

'Look,' said Richard patiently, with the air of one who has thought a problem through thoroughly, 'you don't fall out of bed do you? I mean, have you *ever* rolled over in the night and plummeted out of bed?'

'No,' I admitted reluctantly.

'Well, then you've obviously got an inbuilt sense of whether you are at the edge of the bed or not and you don't go any further. It doesn't matter whether the drop is six inches or six feet, the fact remains you do *not* roll out of bed. And I certainly won't.'

'Why not?'

'Because I'm sleeping against the wall!'

Just before my contract at Peterlee College expired I found another temporary lifeline: to teach at a comprehensive school just down the road from college for half a term because of a maternity leave. The subjects were Home Economics and Needlework, and, though I hadn't been near a sewing machine in a decade, I reckoned I could manage anything for half a term. I knew in my heart though that temporary reprieves were not the answer and that I really had to find work that was full-time, permanent and secure. If that meant turning my back on the teaching profession, as Sandee had done, well, so be it.

Leaving the School of Special Needs on the last day of term was something I found extraordinarily painful to do, not just because it marked the end of a brief period of financial security, but because I had formed relationships with the staff and students alike that I was going to miss, and because I'd found the work more enjoyable and fulfilling than anything I had previously tackled. I had, as they say, found my niche.

Certain pennies, I have found, keep turning up over and over again in life's small change. During the Easter break I got a phone call.

'Carol? It's Sandee. How are you doing? Have you got a job yet?'

'Not full-time,' I admitted ruefully. 'There's absolutely nothing going at the colleges. I think that, like you, I'm going to have to have a re-think. We can't survive forever with me picking up crumbs of work here and there.'

'How radical are you prepared to be?' Sandee asked in a mysterious fashion.

I answered with considerable cautiousness. 'Why?'

'Well, it's just that we've been starting quite a few new projects here recently and I now have several helpers on the housing project here on ET.'

'ET? Isn't that a film about aliens?'

'Not *that* ET! *Government* ET- Employment Training!'

'Oh!' I answered, not really any the wiser.

'It's like the YTS but for an older age group of unemployed people.'

'Ah.'

'I've pointed out that if we could provide the proper theoretical training for them, we could run our own ET scheme – not just limited to social care, such as I'm doing, but to other areas such as the elderly and the handicapped.'

'Ah,' I was obviously no longer fooling Sandee, she twigged I hadn't a clue what she was talking about.

'Carol! Are you listening? We are advertising a full-time job next week for someone to be an ET trainer and supervisor. Preferably someone with a training or teaching background . . . Someone with a background of working in Further Education . . . Someone familiar with the workings of City and Guilds . . . Someone capable of setting up the Community Care Course . . . Someone like *you* – if you're interested!'

The job of course, meant moving into the business biorhythm rather than the academic biorhythm of life: nine-to-five instead of nine-to-four; four weeks' holiday a year (*four* weeks!) instead of nearly three months; no long summer break. How would Richard and the horses survive without me at shows? How would I survive without going to shows with Richard and the horses? How would any of us survive if I didn't get a secure job soon? I sent for the application forms and before we left for our first two battles of the season, Brighton and Windsor, I knew that on my return it would be to an office in Consett with Sandee as my boss. I had a 'proper job'.

Suddenly, after the months of waiting and preparation, those battles were upon us. Brighton was always the most symbolic event for our annual calendar: it was the first event, it was a very tough course, it was a no-holds-barred international competition and it somehow set the tone for the whole of the forthcoming year. Spring – renewal – continuity.

This year it symbolized something else in addition, Richard's return to the driving world after the horrors of the previous season. The unspoken fear that hung between us was, could he do it or had he lost his nerve? For one who had only two-and-a-half-months previously been unable to walk without crutches he had made unbelievable progress. He'd been driving out the horses at home regularly and hard and in all sorts of diabolical weather.

Our journey to Brighton was uneventful if rather strange, as we had had to hire a driver to get the horsebox there, the journey being far too long and arduous for Richard's leg to take. Stamner awaited us with its usual spring welcome and glorious weather and already the park was beginning to show signs of healing and regrowth from the terrible devastation of the October hurricane of two years ago. At least the splintered and mangled corpses of the trees had been removed and the skyline, although still strangely sparse and open, was at least green instead of a broken, jagged brown. I hoped it omened well for our own rebirth from devastation.

Our new trailer home was a dream of space and comfort

beyond anything I'd ever experienced at an event before. I could sit on the deeply cushioned benches by the large picture window at the front, feast my eyes on bright blue sky, springy green grass, fluffy white clouds, pale pink cherry blossom and horse flesh, horse flesh, horse flesh in every direction.

The dressage test day went off surprisingly well with no more than the usual 'pre-test' nerves and jitters, and we were quite satisfied with achieving a respectable fourth place. Marathon day was going to be a different matter: that was where we were going to discover whether Richard Smith was still a pairs driver first and foremost or, indeed, whether he was still a driver at all.

As the morning ticked by my nerves buckled under the strain and I hardly dared look at Richard because I knew the tension was reaching a critical level for him. He had walked the hazards with Helen as repeatedly as his damaged leg would permit and then spent a very restless night, trying, I suspect, to walk them all over again in his sleep. Bear and Blizzard had performed well in the dressage for him and now, for what was a gruelling five-phase marathon, he was putting his hopes – and faith – into his two most experienced marathon horses, Bear and Heather. Experience, stamina and guts, that was what Stamner demanded of horses and drivers alike.

In an almost church-like hush, the grooms began putting on the harness about half an hour before Richard's start time. Of Richard I could see nothing. Alarmed, I scouted around the horsebox and the immediate area to no avail. That only left the trailer and that was where I found him, sitting quite motionless, quite white, as if he was almost frozen to the spot.

'Richard?' I enquired gently.

'I can't do it: I just can't do it. I can't go out there and get on that cart and do it.' It was very obvious that he had reached his moment of truth.

I slid gently into the seat on the other side of the table so I was facing him and closed my hands gently over his tightly clenched ones.

'You don't *have* to. It's as simple as that, Richard, you don't *have* to. Everyone here would understand why you've taken that decision. No one would think any the less of you for it. Good Lord, I've had countless people come up to me in the last couple of days and say it's lovely to see you here, but they never expected it so soon. Several have said they think you're quite *mad* for attempting a marathon at all after such major surgery on your leg. You don't have to prove anything to them – or me – or yourself. You don't *have* to go.'

He raised his head slowly then and gave me a look that was pure, tortured anguish. 'Oh but I do,' he said softly. 'I *do* have to do it: maybe more importantly than anything I've done in my life before.'

'Only you,' I told him as I slid from my seat to leave, 'can make that decision. It's yours and yours alone and whatever it is we will all respect and abide by it.'

I left him to his thoughts and went to see an extremely anxious Helen. 'I think,' I warned her, 'that Richard's nerve may have gone: now that he really has it to face, it's hitting him hard. We must be prepared not to react wrongly if he decides not to go.'

'I thought that might happen,' Helen agreed unhappily. 'He's been pushing himself so hard at home, but it's never the same as at a real event, and some of those hazards out there are – excuse my French – bastards. I know the horses can do it; I'm sure he can do it; but *he's* not sure he can do it – that's the vital point. What do you think I should do? Unharness the horses?'

'No, no,' I said quickly. 'Not yet anyway. That would be an act of treachery somehow. He'd feel dreadful.'

'He'll feel worse when he comes out of there and sees them all ready to go and he can't take them.'

We were both shuffling our feet with indecision and unhappiness when the trailer door flew open and Richard descended, not gracefully, but very purposefully down the steps. He was beaming broadly in a very close imitation of the real thing. 'Come on, come on,' he chided.'Where are my horses? Why aren't they in the vehicle? We've only ten minutes left!'

On cue and without a word, the grooms backed the cobs out of their stalls and took them over to the vehicle.

'Richard, are you *sure*? Are you sure you're going to be all right? You do not *have* to do this.'

'I'll be all right,' he reassured me firmly. 'Quite fine once we get going.'

'But Richard, you . . .' I was the one that was anguished now.

'I'll be all right,' he repeated. 'Now don't you worry. Promise?'

I nodded unconvincingly.

Back in the trailer I tried, and failed, to occupy myself constructively for nearly two hours until he was due to come back into sight in the park and do the hazards. I felt physically ill: tight chest, thumping heart, burning stomach.

After an eternity and yet all too quickly, there was a polite tap at the door and our YTS groom Karen put her head round to ask, 'Mrs Smith, are you going to watch the hazards? It's time.'

Truly I wanted to say no: truly I wanted to curl up on the cushions and shut my heart and mind to what was happening outside. But that would be a total betrayal of Richard, of the horses, of the girls. However painful, however hard, I had to go and watch.

On legs that would have been more at home on a jelly-baby, I walked slowly over the grass to the middle of the park. From there I could see Richard driving most of the earlier hazards at a distance and the final hazards close to. To stand would have been quite out of the question and I sank thankfully on to the short springy grass of the Sussex Downs and asked myself for the thousandth time, *why* are we doing this? Can the risks possibly be justified in any way? What if he damages that fragile and newly healed leg still further? What if . . .? What if . . .?

I must have presented a strange sight, kneeling on the grass, muttering away in a strange mixture of prayer, anger and fear. I plucked relentlessly at the grass, crushing the short sweet blades between my fingers and with them handfuls of the tiny periwinkles that reflected quite perfectly the flawless blue of the May sky. I became aware of people giving me odd looks. I locked myself into silent immobility by an effort of sheer will.

And then they were there: a moving russet blur that drew slowly nearer.

I followed every twist and turn of their movement in those outer hazards with a blessed degree of detachment from reality provided by the distance. It was like watching a silent film.

Encouraged by the simple fact that he had got through those outer hazards safely and without difficulty, I was able to bear the strain of the nearer hazards much better. This was no detached picture; I could hear the clash of harness on metal, the clattering rumble of wheels, the voices from the carriage directing, encouraging. 'Come round! Come round! Steady Bear! Steady! Get on! Get on!' One last tight twist, a canter to the exit gate and the final hazard was behind him and he was trotting fast and straight for the finish line.

Revitalized and obedient again, my legs carried me puffing and pounding behind the carriage. I didn't care what their times were, I didn't care whether they dropped a dozen places on the scoreboard – Richard had broken through a barrier that morning that I had truly thought was going to prove insurmountable, a barrier of memory and fear and pain.

Richard and the horses were reunited.

I was deeply relieved and very, very proud. All the confidence, all the hope that had been entrusted in us by the bank manager, friends and medical staff had come to fruition. Only one major obstacle lay in the path of Richard's return to the very top of the sport he loved and lived for – the lack of a sponsor. That we must now concentrate all our efforts on finding one was the daunting task that preoccupied me as I walked back to the horsebox beside the lathered and still gently blowing horses. I didn't deceive myself it was going to be easy.

It was not the most auspicious start for a season. After our modest success of fourth place at Brighton we were actually eliminated at Royal Windsor because Richard made the unheard-of error of taking a gate in the wrong sequence in a hazard. I wondered and worried if his mind was totally concentrated on the competition or if side issues and pressures were distracting him.

The return from these first two shows marked a turning-point in my life, or at least a violent fork on to a parallel track. No more was I free to wander the country gypsy-like all summer: new responsibilities, new ties, new restrictions bound me: office hours nine to five, five days a week, four weeks' holiday a year. I wasn't totally convinced I was going to survive the experience.

The first week, which coincided with a heat wave, left me drained and bewildered. The days seemed endless and unstructured without a 'school bell' to punctuate them and my body, used to twenty years of academic biorhythm, switched off abruptly at 4.00 pm each day. Precisely what I was meant to be doing I wasn't quite sure – though I pretended I was – but I found myself with one flip chart, one black marker pen and a rented Methodist Sunday School room. Without Sandee's encouraging presence I think I would have simply crawled away defeated after the first couple of weeks.

The middle part of the season began to bite. We were conscious of money – or the lack of it – in everything we did. We were desperately trying to keep the horses' budget down to an absolute minimum so as to make the least possible demands on the overdraft. Every oat was weighed, every stray wisp of hay and straw used. The demands of three large, healthy animals are also large and healthy, and they simply had to have shoes and beds and feed and worming. The diesel bills to the far-flung venues of events were horrendous and we lived in constant fear of a repetition of the mechanical trouble with the horsebox of the previous season. I longed to indulge the horses in the things they so richly deserved – gleaming leather headcollars with their names on brass plates, and heavy Melton rugs. Instead, they had to make do with shabby webbing collars and tatty old rugs, as they could not now appear in their smart 'Montan' liveries at shows. I was sweeping fiercely at the concrete in the yard one day, with a brush that at one end was down to the bare wooden head, when a saying of Great-aunt Meg's swam into my mind. 'As daft as a brush with no hairs on' she would say with contempt about any endeavour that seemed pointless or any object that appeared useless. It had always struck me as an odd saying and one I couldn't quite fathom. Until that moment.

Then it hit me with such clarity and force I actually gasped and stopped in my sweeping. How daft were we? Hundreds, *thousands* of pounds would be spent before the year was out: all money we didn't have, all poured down the endless drain called 'driving'. And we didn't even have the obvious basic requirement – a firm financial footing from which to achieve any of it. We didn't even have a shaky one. We didn't even have a yard brush with a full head of hair.

Meanwhile the great parting of the ways happened for the first time: Richard, the horses and the grooms left for Scotland. I stayed at home, stoic but hurting like mad, to go to work. It was only three days, he consoled, I would be driving up to join them in Scotland on the Friday night.

Yes, getting there at bed time and leaving again Sunday lunchtime to get back for work, I felt like replying slightly bitterly.

At Islabank, which we had won for the previous three years, we came a very close second to the winner and were delighted. Then at Holker, that most demanding of Lakeland events, we were well in contention and flying through the second to last hazard, the water splash, when the carriage quite simply snapped in two. One second Helen was standing on the back step and the next she plunged forward towards Richard, her legs miraculously just missing being crushed between the twisting buckling, collapsing metal. It was the old, old problem. The good cross-country vehicle had belonged to Alan Robson in the Montan era and had been returned to him at the end of it. We were coping once more with inferior home-made equipment and the strains and stresses of the course were just too much for it. It was a crushing blow to morale and the lack of confidence spilt over into the next event, Kelso, where Richard came in, almost unbelievably, in ninth position. We had had no problems, no harness snap, no vehicle collapsing, no horses misbehaving, no driver error. He had simply come ninth.

The atmosphere was so strained and tense that quarrels began to break out. Richard and Helen were at loggerheads, Richard and I were at loggerheads. When we came a disappointing 'also ran' place at Sandringham, Richard announced enough was enough. He was throwing in the towel. He obviously wasn't going to be able to stage the comeback he'd hoped for. The fault obviously lay with him and he was letting all of us down; the horses, the girls and me. He had driven his last event.

The ensuing grief on the yard and amongst the girls was so genuine and unbearable that, with great reluctance on his part, we finally persuaded him to have one more go.

This one was the bogey: Lowther.

Once again Richard would have to drive, not the exact hazards, but the exact ground of his accident the year before. This was the one he *had* to do, and do well, if the bogey was to be laid to rest forever.

He used the 'old firm' of horses of course, needing all the experience we could muster. His dressage was excellent, putting him in a marginal second place behind the leader. The hazards flowed effortlessly behind him. Heart in mouth and tears in eyes I watched him tackle them one by one and all the memories of flashing blue lights and wailing sirens were blotted out as he flew swiftly and accurately through them, the horses full of fire, energy and the will to win.

Only one hazard left to go, only *one* hazard and then he would be home, surely to his second place, even, possibly, to victory. I had to choose between viewing that last hazard and being at the finish line and I knew the latter was where I really wanted to be. I trotted off, filled with relief and excitement, and waited by the red and white flags that marked the end of the course. The waiting was too long.

When, finally, a pair of horses did appear, panic flooded me – it was not Richard. Half-way back to the final hazard I came across Richard and Helen, each leading a horse. At least they were all safe, my mind acknowledged, but my mouth had to ask 'What happened?'

'Stub axle,' Richard said wearily. 'Simply sheared off in

the last hazard and we lost the wheel – quite simple really, vehicle just not up to it.' He trudged pass me, his head and shoulders bent with the weight of his sorrow and his humiliation. He was limping very badly.

Back at the horsebox, the atmosphere was what can only be described as funereal. We were all in mourning. We all knew we had just experienced the death of our most cherished hopes. I cried, I ranted, I raged at the fates that would allow a single piece of metal to disintegrate a few hundred yards before the line that marked the distinction between victory and defeat.

But it was in vain and it was quite useless. As Richard pointed out, if the vehicle hadn't collapsed this week it would have done it at the next show – or the next. It was unreliable; *he* was unreliable. Everything was unreliable. We had played out our luck too hard and too long. Perhaps God had been trying to give a timely warning the year before when Richard crushed his leg. Perhaps losing our sponsor should have brought us to the end of the road. We had defied the fates and continued blindly – perhaps even arrogantly. Now we were left with ashes.

And to sweep them up, only a brush with no hairs on.

13

The Last Stand

Back home, we licked our wounded pride, welded up the home-made boneshaker for the umpteenth time and tried to think coherently. We also sustained another loss: Helen left us after Lowther; she'd been with us nearly two years, most of it fraught with disaster and uncertainty, and so we couldn't possibly blame her when she took up the offer of full-time, better paid and totally secure work in another driving yard.

This meant we were left with our second-year YTS groom, Karen, and a very inexperienced newcomer on the YTS, Lesley. We were also left with three horses who were at the peak of fitness and keenness, and one event left on the annual driving calendar: the National Championships at Windsor.

It had been a crushing year. All the letters I had written and leads I had followed over sponsorship had come to naught, a box full of polite, declining letters in return was all. We had had little or no success on the annual circuit – our worst season ever, actually, with one small win and one decent second our best scores. I *needed* something posi-tive and of recognizable value to wave, a banner to put under noses saying 'Look! Look at us! This is what we are!' No one was going to sponsor us on what we had been.

Windsor really was the last event, the last of the money. The last stand. And, we decided after much heart-searching, we did have to make that stand: however hard. We had to come out fighting for what could truly be the last competition for the horses; if we didn't we might never forgive ourselves in years to come. We had undertaken to do the season – we had to finish it.

Once it was made, I was pleased with the decision: to have thrown in the towel earlier in the year with the string of miserable mistakes and poor scores, or after Lowther's humiliating climax, would have left a bitter taste in our mouths for the rest of our days. If we were going down, we were going down fighting.

The brunt of the responsibility and work of getting organized to go, keeping horses fit and well and looking after them at the shows, all fell on Karen's young and relatively inexperienced shoulders. I cursed the fact that I had to go off to work each morning and leave the horses and all connected with them behind for Richard and Karen to struggle on with alone.

It wasn't that I disliked the job, in fact I was quite enjoying it and had things well organized and running smoothly now. It was just that there were other, more important things in my life that were now having to take back seat to this 'earning a living' business. I had managed to organize my meagre rations of annual holiday so that I could take a few days off around the Nationals and that was some small consolation. How I longed for the 'academic' year where at least I would be free to wander all summer.

On our arrival at Windsor, the horses were well and fit, the weather was warm and kind, Karen rose to her new position of head groom with astonishing maturity and ability. She shone with the responsibility that had been thrust upon her. The dressage test went very well, leaving us in contention, and on marathon day Richard took his old friend Ray Brown's son Geoffrey with him as shotgun: his experience in handling the back of a cart and his muscular strength were much greater than Karen's.

At the start of the marathon we experienced our first panic of the event. Richard was driving Heather and Blizzard for that phase and I walked down, as was my custom, to see them off at the start, which was some quarter of a mile from where we were parked. Such a filthy and indignant look did Bear give me as I set off, that I took pity on him, tied up there alone and forlorn in the stalls, undid his lead rope and took him with me to the start.

As I chatted about the course with Richard, a pleasant lady who announced herself as our referee, approached the carriage. Brief introductions were made and then she climbed on board.

'Oh, you'd better give me my numbers,' she said politely.

'Mr Smith – five minutes!' said the starting official firmly. Panic! Each competitor is identified on the marathon by a large yellow 'number plate' which is inserted into a transparent bib and displayed, back and front, by the referee sitting alongside the driver. The rules are quite simple, but quite firm. No number, no go. We had left them behind in the horsebox! The ruling on the start time for each competitor is equally firm. That clock would start running for Richard in exactly five minutes. What to do?

I had a brief, heroic vision of me leaping astride my valiant steed, bareback with only a halter rope for steering, and galloping off to the rescue. This momentary lunacy was replaced by the more down to earth fact that I stood no chance whatsoever of struggling astride Bear bareback – and with no mane to hold on to and no reins to steer with I stood little chance of staying on board even if I could.

Richard was trying to bluster it out with the official, but I knew it was to no avail.

'Don't worry I'll get them!' I yelled valiantly and tugged at Bear's lead rein.

'Four minutes!' rang in my ears as we set off at a fast jog.

Bear was quite astounded; he obviously thought I'd finally fallen off my trolley, but decided he would go along with the little game as it was actually quite good fun.

I did attract a few queer looks as I puffed and pounded determinedly back through the stable compound gates. My obviously fitter and much more elegantly athletic companion jogging politely alongside with an expression that clearly said 'I'm not with her!' My lungs, legs and stamina held out until we reached the box, but it took the last of the wind out of my sails to yell 'Karen! The marathon numbers! Quick!'

Even as she scampered frantically into the horsebox to retrieve them I knew there was absolutely no way that I could make it back to Richard at the start on time – not without inducing a terminal coronary. Karen would have to run back with them herself. Even then, I anguished, could she possibly make it? More than two minutes must have passed since I'd set off on my mission. I'd failed them – oh defeat! Oh despair!

A small grey creature ambled across the front of the wagon. It was one of Jill Holah's ponies, Cirius, out for a leg stretch with Anna, the young girl who helped Jill exercise her small but dynamic duo.

'Got them!' yelled Karen, thundering down the ramp. I snatched the plastic objects from her hands as I thrust Bear's lead rope into them.

'Anna!' I gasped. 'Get these down to Richard at the start of the marathon, do you understand? He's due to start any minute now and he can't go without them! Don't take any notice of the man at the gate: just go, Anna, GO!'

'Right,' she grinned, snatching the numbers from me.

'Hi ho, Silver! Away!' wasn't in it. The super fit little

pony did a three-hundred-and-sixty degree turn where he stood and accelerated from 0 to 60 in about two seconds flat. He was cantering before he even got to the gate, where an indignant security man could only yell 'Oy!' at a set of twinkling silver shoes. Up at the start of the marathon, Richard was in despair.

'Thirty seconds, Mr Smith – and I'm afraid I'll have to start the clock.'

Equally anxious, Geoff Brown was all for setting off himself to find out what had happened to me, but as he scanned the horizon hopelessly, he saw a small shape moving like a white blur right up the middle of the historic Windsor long mile. 'Richard!' he reported. 'I think your numbers are arriving!'

Bent low over Cirius's neck, reins in one hand and the precious numbers in the other, Anna was up in her stirrups and going as if the entire Apache nation was after her. As Cirius's little legs drummed along in flat-out gallop, Geoff said afterwards that you could almost hear the bugles sounding. Any potential Pony Club Olympic team should not even be considered without young Anna and Cirius.

'Ten seconds!'

Geoffrey leant out the back of the carriage.

'Five seconds!'

The cobs began to trot up to the start and Anna hauled Cirius to a more manageable pace.

'Four . . . three . . .'

Leaning right out of her saddle, Anna stretched across to Geoffrey, who snatched the numbers and plonked them over an astounded referee's neck. Anna curved away out of the path of the carriage just as the horses accelerated and the official starter recovered briefly enough to say '. . . two . . . one . . . away!'

Grinning from ear to ear, Anna trotted sedately back to camp and, after giving her and Cirius a big hug, I thought it only right that I was the one to explain to Jill why her immaculate grey pony had gone out for a gentle hack, but had returned steaming and mud-besplattered after being press-ganged into joining the Pony Express.

The marathon was a close run thing, as were the cones – a very close run thing. And with our oldest and most respected rival just out in front, what could we do? Stand next to her in the final line up and receive our second place award with pride, with delight and with hearts newly ablaze with hope, of course.

'The National Pair Driving Champion, 1989: Christine Dick.

Reserve National Champion: Richard Smith.'

I had my banner to wave.

The horses had their annual October holiday and, in relays, the girls took time off likewise. For the first time in five years we were without an employed groom. Nor were we looking to employ one. I was still writing letters, following leads and hoping, but nothing concrete or even remotely solid had turned up.

Early November marked the annual competitors' conference down at Stoneleigh and normally I would have accompanied Richard, but Karen was on holiday and Lesley was far too inexperienced to cope on her own. Richard organized to stay with friends on the Saturday night, but promised to be back on the Sunday after the conference ended, even if it was very late at night, as he knew I had to be at work the next morning.

I helped Lesley put the horses to bed at teatime and checked them myself for peace of mind before going to bed. Lesley was a strange young woman. She was approaching twenty-one years of age and yet it would have been easier to put her physically and emotionally at around fourteen or fifteen. She was diminutive in height, Yorkshire in accent, wore her long brown hair in a single plait, and wore no makeup or clothes other than jeans and a jumper.

The sole focus of her life was her twenty-three-year-old Dartmoor pony, Major, which had had to accompany her to us before she would accept a placement. She was reasonably thorough at her work, though openly nervous about riding the 'big horses', but never showed any real commitment or emotional attachment to the cobs. All of those emotions, all her enthusiasm, every waking second that she wasn't actually working were invested in her pony, which, because of her own diminutive size she could still easily ride. She was a Peter Pan – well, a Petra Pan – stuck in the groove of early adolescence and unwilling, or afraid, to travel any further towards adulthood and its responsibilities.

On the Sunday morning I allowed myself the luxury of an extra half an hour lie in, but could hear from the banging of buckets that Lesley had actually started on the morning stables. I peered through the curtains and when a pleasant morning was revealed, hopped into a tracksuit and went out to help with the mucking out with genuine enthusiasm. The worst feature of my new 'office job' was the hours I now sat immobile in artificial light and heat in front of a desk. The weekends, with the opportunity to get 'stuck in' with the horses, had become not only emotionally but physically essential.

'Morning, Lesley.'

'Morning, Mrs Smith.'

'Everything all right?'

'Fine, Mrs Smith.'

The first box I peered into was Heather's. She had her backside towards me and I was chiding her for her ungraciousness when I noticed her morning ration of hay, untouched, on the floor. Everything Donald Waite had told us about Heather when he sold her to us had been totally true. Including the fact that she 'were a good doer; loves 'er grub does Heather.'

'Heather?' I enquired softly, opening the door and entering her stable. 'What's up with you big lady? It's not like you to leave your breakfast.' She never even turned at my approach or voice, but just stood there, head hanging listlessly. I took hold of her headcollar to turn her into the light so I could see her better, but although her head moved, her body didn't follow. She just stood her ground. Patting her, I went back outside and, when a suitable distance from the box, bellowed 'Lesley!'

There was a scrabbling noise from the muckheap beyond the gate and then Lesley appeared.

'Yes, Mrs Smith?' she asked anxiously.

'Why didn't you tell me at once there was something wrong with Heather?'

'Heather?' she said, mystified. 'I've given her her hay and water.'

'And?' I demanded.

'And?' she repeated, parrot-like.

'What did she *do* with them?' I asked, trying to sound more reasonable.

'Do?' she was still mystified.

'What does she *normally* do with her hay?' I asked, trying very hard to keep my temper.

'Oh, eat it, Mrs Smith.'

'Yes. Well done, Lesley. But today,' I propelled her swiftly over to the box, 'not only has she not eaten it, she hasn't even touched it. Doesn't that strike you as strange? And where was she when you put her feed and water in?'

'In her box, Mrs smith.'

'Yes, but *where* in her box, Lesley?' I was going to scream in a minute.

She paused briefly over the door. 'Just where she is now.'

'Just? You mean *exactly*?'

'Well, I think so,' Lesley replied miserably.

'She didn't want to come over and say good morning? She wasn't breaking her neck over the door to get her breakfast – like she does every morning God sends her? Did that not strike you as odd?'

'Well, I suppose so, now that you mention it.'

'How *long* is it since you fed round, Lesley?'

'I started about an hour ago as usual, Mrs Smith.'

'And you've been backwards and forwards past that box umpteen times since and all that time that mare *has never moved*?'

'I didn't notice, Mrs Smith.' Lesley answered miserably but honestly.

'Lesley,' I said exasperated, 'if we are ever to make a responsible, employable groom out of you the first thing, the most important thing, is to *know* the horses in your care. Know their habits, know their routines and any changes in those habits, then *worry* – and report it!'

'Yes, Mrs Smith.'

'Well, come on then, let's find out what on earth is wrong with her.'

With enormous reluctance, me pulling and Lesley pushing, Heather walked slowly out on to the yard. That she was badly lame was apparent when she took her first step and even Lesley could spot the affected leg at once. The off-side hind; swollen and puffy round the fetlock and hot to the touch.

'Whoa, big lass,' I crooned as I lifted the affected foot into my arm to examine it. Even flexing the foot to lift it seemed to cause her pain and she trembled slightly. I examined the sole of her foot quickly but thoroughly and with a hoof pick checked for simple but obvious causes such as a stone in her hoof. But there was no sign of foreign bodies, no sign of a puncture wound, no white chipped areas to indicate a bruised sole. I moved into the bulbs of her heel. Heather has a very small 'boxy' foot for such a large lady and her heels have a deep cleavage in them. At the top of this crevasse there was a small suppurating sore – rather like a cold sore – but quite tiny, no more than a nick really. Certainly nothing I would have classed as a 'cracked heel'. I replaced her foot gently on the ground and felt round the coronet and then up the tendons. The whole of the joint was warm and inflamed and yet the tendons didn't seem to be involved in any way.

'We'll try the simple remedies first,' I told Lesley. 'Something that can do no harm and may do a lot of good. I can't find anything external that's wrong – cuts or gashes or punctures. She could have simply strained it carrying on in the field somehow. Go and fix the hosepipe, that's a good girl.'

Lesley trotted off and a minute or so later I was playing a stream of cold water over the affected foot.

'There now,' I said comfortingly to Heather. 'Let's see if that makes it feel better.'

After half an hour, when the injury should have reduced greatly in swelling and pain, neither of these hopeful results had occurred and Heather still would hardly take a step. I also knew, in my heart, that a sprain in itself, though painful, shouldn't have put her off her food. 'Second rule,' I said to Lesley when we'd helped Heather painfully back to her box, 'when in doubt, call the vet.'

He was there by about 11.00 o'clock.

A new vet to us, this Trevor Hall, Mr Peacock having retired from large animal practice the year before. He was young, into alternative medicines and horses and travelled everywhere with his pure white husky dog for company in his four-wheel-drive vehicle. He also had, he claimed, clairvoyant powers.

'Chestnut mare, eh?' he said thoughtfully as he strode up the yard. He looked carefully over the door for a few seconds before opening it. 'No, she's not the one.'

'Not the one?' I said, mystified.

'Not the one that's going to kill me,' he said quite lightly.
'I've had this premonition I'll be killed by a chestnut mare.
She has four white socks and there'll be a church with a
strange square tower in the background and more than
that I don't know. Not that,' he added quickly as he ran
expert fingers down the back of her leg, 'it would stop me
coming in to help her even if I thought she *was* the one.
You can't change your destiny. Pointless.

'When did you notice this?'

I was so taken aback I had to refocus my mind.

'Eh? Oh, about two hours ago – just before I phoned. Do
you want her outside?'

'No, no. She obviously doesn't want to move, so why
make her? Listen to the patient I always say.'

'What's wrong with her?' I beseeched.

'Well, from the look of that leg and her temperature . . .'
he removed a thermometer from her rear and examined it
closely '. . . I'd say mud fever.'

'Mud fever? Mud fever! But we haven't *got* any mud at
this time of the year. The ground is solid out there and her
legs are quite clean.'

'Nothing to do with mud. Misnomer really. More to do
with micro-organisms in the soil that get into the system
through the tiniest of wounds – probably that scratch on
her heel there, see it?'

'Yes, I found that this morning.'

'Well the body sets up a toxic reaction to the micro-
organism, swelling, pain, temperature and – Bingo – lame
and not very well horse.' He was removing syringes and
bottles from his bag now and preparing an injection. 'I was
once called out to destroy a horse that was found in its
box with its leg so horribly swollen and in such terrible
agony that they thought it must have broken its leg in the
night. The leg wasn't broken at all. Mud fever: that's what
it was. An acute toxic reaction. It recovered right as rain

after treatment. In an earlier age it would have been dead: either shot for its broken leg or out of its mind with the agony.'

I shuddered.

'But she . . . Oh, she ought to be fine once those drugs take effect. A large dose of antibiotics and an anti-inflammatory to help her discomfort. Keep an eye on her. If you're worried, phone me. I should be at home this afternoon, up the dale.'

'I will and thank you. I hate dragging a vet out on a weekend or late at night.'

'My patients don't keep diaries,' he said loading his equipment back in the car, 'and I never mind being called out if there's a genuine reason, never.'

'Food?' I asked finally.

'Like you, she'll eat when she's hungry. Keep water at her though, with the chill off. It'll help her temperature.'

'Thank you again.'

He was off, his furry white friend lolling his tongue out of the window in farewell.

'Mrs Smith?'

'Yes, Lesley.'

'The stables are all done and horses all turned out – except Heather of course. Would it be all right if I took Major for a ride?'

It was a lovely day and it was Sunday. None of this was Lesley's *fault* and it was *all* my responsibility.

'Have you checked Heather?' I asked sternly.

'Oh yes,' she affirmed. 'She still hasn't eaten, but she's passed muck and had some water. I've topped up her bucket.'

'Good girl, Lesley – very observant. Yes, go for your ride and enjoy it. I really must finish emptying the trailer out before the winter sets in or it will never get done. We'll have some lunch when you get back.'

She went off happily and, despite her reassurances, I

went to the loosebox to check on Heather myself. There was no apparent change and I bent myself to the unpleasant but necessary task of emptying cupboards and drawers. It was time-consuming work and I realized with a jolt as I staggered through the door with yet another load of driving paraphernalia for winter storage that the clock stood at 1.30. I hadn't even noticed Lesley return up the back street on her pony. Surely she must be back after two hours? Alarmed, I put down the box I was carrying and went on to the yard. As soon as I went through the gate I could see Major tied up to the wall right next to Heather's loosebox, where Lesley was totally engrossed in the thorough grooming she was giving him, talking away to him as one would to a close friend as she worked. And perhaps he is her only close friend, I thought suddenly.

'Nice ride?'

'Oh lovely, thanks.'

'Good, good. And how's Heather?'

I skirted round the opposite side of the pony to the one she was grooming and peered in the box.

'Oh my God!' I howled, scattering both the pony and Lesley as I flung open the door, and flew into the box. 'Heather! Heather!'

She was stretched across the floor of the box, her breath coming in painful rasps. The leg, which only two hours previously had been swollen to the ankle, was now a solid pillar of thickened flesh beyond her hock, obscenely gross compared to her other three slim limbs.

'Lesley!' I screamed.

She appeared at the door. 'Shall I just put Major in the . . .?'

'Oh sod Major!' I flung at her. 'Get in here!' White with alarm she approached.

'Whatever's the matter?' she said, horrified.

'I don't *know* what's the matter, I don't *know*. But how long has she been like this? Was she like this when you

got back from your ride? How long ago was *that*?' I was
vicious from fear, and guilt too, knowing that it had been
two hours since I'd last checked her. I needed a scapegoat.

'I don't know, Mrs Smith,' tears were welling and splash-
ing down Lesley's face now. 'I didn't look. I just thought
she'd be all right after the vet had been.'

'You didn't look! You didn't look!' I raged, I wailed. 'You
mean you rode that stupid little pony into this yard, tied
it to her door post and you never even *looked* to see if she
was all right? You never even *noticed* she was flat on the
floor? She's dying six feet away from you and you never
even noticed! Does she have to lie here with four legs in
the air before you notice *anything*?'

'Dying?' she gulped, horrified. 'Oh no!'

I'd meant it as a figure of speech, but kneeling by the
mare's sweaty neck and listening to her rasping breath I
realized that this was, unbelievably, what we were witness-
ing. Lesley was backing out the door now.

'Come here,' I said more gently. She was close to panick-
ing and running. 'Come on, quickly, quickly. That's it, kneel
here. Right, just talk to her Lesley, do you understand?
Talk to her. I'll get the vet.'

Not since all those years previously when Bear's life had
hung by a thread in that terrible septic tank had my hand
trembled so much as I dialled a number. 'Mr Hall?' I gab-
bled the split second the phone was picked up.

'No, it's his housekeeper,' said a middle-aged lady's
voice.

'He is there, isn't he?' I asked, panic-stricken.

'Yes, he is,' she replied in a tone that indicated clearly
that it *was* Sunday afternoon.

'Tell him to come straight away. Mrs Smith, Mount
Pleasant Farm, Stanley Crook. It's the chestnut mare he
saw this morning. She's down and her breathing is terrible.
Tell him . . .' I paused, almost unable to say the words. 'Tell
him, I think she's dying.'

'Mrs Smith, Mount Pleasant Farm?' Her response was genuine and swift and then the receiver was plonked down.

I rushed back outside, mouth dry and legs out of control. Major was still tied, rather bemused, to the wall, and Lesley was still on the floor with Heather. I took her place at Heather's head.

'Go and put Major away and see to him.'

'Oh, Mrs Smith,' she sobbed. 'I . . .'

'There's nothing you can do, Lesley and it's *not* your fault. Truly it isn't. I'm sorry for what I said. Now, go and see to Major please and then go and watch out for the vet. Tell me the moment you see him coming up the back lane.'

She left reluctantly and truly I had dismissed her because it was suddenly very vital that I was on my own with Heather. The plain but handsome face was flat on the floor now. So little strength or will did she have that she couldn't even keep her nose out of the straw to breathe, and the weight of her own head was pressing her far side nostril closed against the ground. This made her efforts to breathe even more laboured.

'Oh Heather, Heather!' I crooned as I manoeuvred my knees under her head so that I could lift it up on to my lap and at least keep both her nostrils clear. I ran my fingers up the shorn workman-like crest of her neck to the large floppy ears I had so often teased her about. Her ultra-fine silky coat was darkened with patches of sweat and her rubbery lower lip hung from her mouth, totally flaccid. Her breath was coming in more frequent and shallower gasps, each exhaled with a short grunt that tore into the very soul of me. I loved this gentle but powerful creature, this plain but dignified lady who had come later than Bear and Blizzard to my life and heart, but who had given as much in three years as it was possible for any horse to give. I watched her pulse and saw as the minutes ticked by that it fluttered weaker and weaker on its path up her neck.

'Heather!' It was all I could say, over and over, rocking with grief and impotence. There was nothing I could do but cradle her and cry for her and pray for her.

Where was Richard? Damn him. I glanced at my watch; it was nearly 2 o'clock. Twenty minutes since I had phoned the vet. He lived at Frosterly, some ten miles or so away, but not an easy ten miles, not a flat ten miles. The same journey would take me half an hour. I doubted she had ten minutes left. The breathing was very shallow now and the pulse a faint throb.

'Heather!' I screamed and wept at the empty rafters. 'Don't die! Dear God, don't die sweet lady. The vet will be here soon. Hold on Heather, please, please hold on!' I cursed myself even as I wept for my unseemly weakness. It was not what she deserved. She was slipping away from me in the same manner she had shared her life with us. With great strength and dignity and making no fuss whatsoever.

'He's here!' shrieked Lesley, pounding up the yard.

Brakes screeched, doors slammed, feet ran. He was opening his bag as he entered the stable.

'She's . . .' I began. What was the point of saying anything? It was very obvious.

He felt her neck swiftly and then removed a large syringe and filled it. 'Quickly,' he said imperatively. 'Seconds count. Stretch her head forward so I can get into that vein.' He wasted no more words and plunged the needle deep into her neck.

In fairy tales, the Fairy Godmother touches an object with her wand and then golden light slowly suffuses the object and it is transformed. No sooner had Trevor withdrawn the needle in her neck than Heather's head began to lift of its own volition from my lap. Soon, she was holding it free from me with the strength of her own muscles, blinking slightly as though she was being released from some terrible spell. Then I felt her forelegs begin to twitch.

'Get clear,' Trevor ordered.

It was as if you could follow the path of the drug as it passed, like a magic golden light, through her body. Within a couple of minutes, she was sitting with her forelegs propped up, and a minute after that she had scrambled up, ungainly as a new-born foal, on to all four legs. It was indeed a magical transformation.

'Can I . . .?' I held my arms out.

'Oh yes, yes,' said Trevor. 'I don't think she'll go down again.'

'Heather,' I whispered weakly as I put my arms around her and buried my face in the sweet silky fragrance of her neck. 'You nearly scared me to death.'

I recovered myself in a moment or two and released her to face the vet. 'What,' I enquired, 'was in that syringe?'

'Pure morphine,' he replied. 'She'll be feeling great now.'

'But what *happened*? I mean, what was wrong with her? How could she recover so quickly?'

'She hasn't recovered,' Trevor said grimly. 'All I've done is remove her pain. All that was *wrong* with her was the agony of that leg and the infection. Didn't you know pain can kill?'

'Was she . . .?' I began lamely and awkwardly.

'Dying? Probably . . . she didn't have very much time left. It was the shock that was killing her. A horse with a lesser temperament would have reacted differently. I've seen horses in that much pain simply go mad with it and throw themselves off the walls of their box. She had just, well, resigned herself to it I suppose. She would have had to give up sooner rather than later though.'

'What can we do for her now?' I asked, bringing myself back to the task at hand.

'Well, remember the horse supposed to have a broken

leg? Perhaps that was a premonition I overlooked – remembering about it this morning. She has had an equally violent toxic reaction to the organism that has invaded her body. Look at that leg, it's like a tree trunk. All her immune system is probably poisoned now, trying to fight it, so we must help it. Give her regular doses of broad spectrum antibiotics, something for the infection and of course, keep the pain under control. Beyond that,' he snapped his bag closed, 'well, despite the wonders of modern medicine, we still have to let nature take its course. She's a very poorly lady. She has a high temperature and she's not eating. She's going to need careful nursing.'

'Oh, she'll get that,' I assured him.

A peace of sorts had returned to the yard, but it was a vigilant, uneasy peace. I was frightened literally to leave her for a minute.

After Trevor had gone, I set about making my patient as comfortable as possible. Bale upon bale of straw had been spread and banked around the sides of her box. As the sun went down, so did the thermometer and by late afternoon it was plain that we were in for the first sharp frosty late-autumn night of the year. So, despite her high temperature, I rugged her up lightly with a cotton sweat sheet and a summer-weight rug, leaving the chest fastening open and turned back to help prevent her breaking out in a sweat again. In the early evening Trevor returned to check on her and administer another jab. Since struggling to her feet after the first miraculous shot she had remained motionless and was obviously reluctant to try and move the affected leg. Leave well alone and let her stay where she was, was Trevor's advice. She would move when she was good and ready.

After his second visit he was satisfied that she did seem to be 'stable', her temperature was down slightly and there was every hope that she would not collapse in such a spectacular and horrifying fashion again. If I was worried though, then of course call him. I was taking no chances.

Leaving Lesley standing outside the stable door, on penalty of death if she so much as blinked for too long, I dived into the house to gather what I considered would be the essentials for the long and bitterly cold vigil that lay ahead. God alone knew when Richard would be back – he could even change his mind and decide to stay over after all.

I changed into layers of clothing that began with thermals next to my skin and ended, after various and increasingly cosy layers, with a thick quilted jacket, lined boots, scarf, gloves and, very essential, a woolly hat. Looking like the original Michelin Man, I staggered back out to the stable with an armful that comprised sandwiches, thermos flask, transistor radio, books, newspapers and torch and then returned for the final touches of duvet and – most important of all – a hot-water bottle.

It was bitingly cold and quite dark outside when I put the final touches to my emergency arrangements. Lesley had put all the other horses and ponies to bed and had been despatched to the house to get herself some supper, a warming bath and to be on phone duty – just in case Richard decided to phone home. The clean, banked straw in the far corner of Heather's box made a comfortable and well-insulated nest into which I installed myself.

Duvet over my legs and knees and pulled almost up to my chin, I revelled in the pool of warmth that spread out from the hot-water bottle snuggled in my lap. I read the Sunday papers from cover to cover, consumed my sandwiches and drank my tea. Still it got colder and colder and still Heather never moved other than to shift the weight of her three good legs around to share the load a bit.

I got up to give my own legs a stretch and return some circulation to them and was overjoyed when she accepted a small drink of water when I lifted the bucket and offered it to her. It was the first small, but positive, sign of improvement she had shown. By now it was about 9.00 pm and Lesley came round to do her evening stables – and to report that Richard had not phoned. She kindly offered to refill my tea flask for me and then I suggested it might be a good idea for her to have an early night, as God only knew what the next day would bring.

Only after she'd gone did I regret not asking her to refill my hot-water bottle as well. It was illogical that I could be actually *cold*, given the layers of clothing and insulation that surrounded me, but that rubber bag full of hot water had somehow provided a focus of *actual* heat and comfort that was probably as warming psychologically as it was physically. There is nothing more utterly depressing than a cold hot-water bottle.

So, there I was, trying to convince myself that I was perfectly comfortable, when a small, dark shape sprang over the stable door and landed elegantly in the straw. 'Prrr-owww?' the shape enquired inquisitively, as if to say, 'Hello – what's going on in here?' It was Holly.

I was pathetically glad of her company and support and after a frenzy of scratching ears and tickling her tummy, when I turned back the corner of the duvet, she needed no second bidding. She was, I found, far, far more comforting than the hot-water bottle. Not as *hot*, it was true, but she radiated waves of cosy companionship from her little body – which positively throbbed with purring – and her own small pool of warmth as she lay snuggled on my lap. Together, we saw the vigil into the night. I knew there was probably no earthly point in our being there: Heather had been up on her feet quite unchanged for nearly eight hours.

'If she gets through the night without going down, then we're in with a chance.' I shook my head to clear the muzziness. Had Trevor Hall said that? Or was it another vet, long ago when Bear was going through the most critical night of his life? Well, whoever, I was leaving nothing to chance. I longed to put the stable light out and simply snuggle down in my straw nest with my little cat and go to sleep – proper sleep, instead of the fitful, jerky dozes I was sliding in and out of. But if I put the lights out and slept soundly, I might just fail to detect signs of early distress in the mare and then my vigil would have been pointless. Pulling my hat low over my ears and resigning myself to the fact there was *no* way I could keep the tip of my nose warm, I remained at my post of duty.

It must have been past midnight when I heard footsteps coming up the yard. I tried to struggle to my feet, but my bones had locked up with the unaccustomed hardness and immobility of the last hours.

'Carol?' said Richard anxiously, peering over the stable door.

Holly wriggled out of her cosy lair and jumped up to rub herself against his chest. I struggled with covers and clothing and cramp to try and get upright.

'Oh, Richard – thank goodness you're home.'

'What on earth's going on?' he asked, mystified.

'It's Heather,' I told him. 'She's been so ill, Richard. Really, truly, we nearly lost her this afternoon.'

'Heather?' he repeated incredulously, gazing at the familiar form that was standing very placidly, in other words totally normally, at the back of the box. 'But she looks fine!'

I knew it was going to be hard for him to believe it when he'd not seen it with his own eyes, so slowly and carefully I took him through the day's events and, leading him across the box, allowed him to see for himself the distended leg.

'You go to bed now,' Richard said simply, straightening up from looking at her leg. 'I'll stay with Heather.'

'But you've just been driving for hours,' I protested. 'You must be shattered.'

'And *you*,' he pointed out firmly, 'have to go to work tomorrow. I don't. So go to bed, and no arguing.'

I knew what he said was true. But I also knew that

he probably needed, as I had done, just time alone with Heather.

I left them together and headed for the house with one last anxious glimpse behind me. The stars were winking above the stable in a sky of black ink, and the silhouette of a small cat was outlined on top of the stable door. I left them all to the mercies of the night.

Heather's recovery was not a hasty affair. By the second day her lymphatic system, as Trevor Hall had predicted, struggling with the task of removing so much poison from her body, was suffering from over-load. At all points of her body the lymph glands were distended, and between her back legs the lumpy swellings hung obscenely, like pendulous bunches of grapes. She was very reluctant to move.

For over three days, although the rest of her body was active, she never once lifted the affected leg from the floor. When she did move, it was rather like a four-pronged compass: the three good legs scribing a slow circle with the bad leg remaining firmly fixed at the central point.

She did drink well, thank goodness, her water laced with glucose powder and a little salt to replace the body fluids lost through her fever. Her temperature slowly but steadily fell, and as it did so her appetite slowly and steadily improved.

Towards the end of the first week, she was being led on small regular walks around the block to keep her circulation going and help reduce the swelling. It was a couple of weeks, however, before we deemed it safe to turn her into the field and many, many weeks before we weren't greeted every morning by a leg that looked like a pudding around the fetlock and hock. Dramatic and devastatingly swift had been her decline. Very slowly, the horse that Donald Waite had described to us as 'a tough old bird' determinedly plodded her way back.

As she did so, a new drama began to unfold, this time

at a pace that was as unhurried as Heather's recovery. However, the implications of its path became as devastating as Heather's collapse, the possible journey's-end of its course almost unthinkable.

That long path began with one simple statement: 'I didn't think Bear was quite level today.'

14

Driving Finish

The race was nearly over and somehow I just couldn't find the heart for the final furlong. It had been a race against time and disastrous odds with only one far-sighted bank manager foolish enough to put a stake on us at all. Well, we were just about around the circuit of the year since he had invested that faith in us and then the race would be over. The handicaps we were carrying were simply overwhelming; there was nothing left for a final heroic driving finish to the line. Quite the opposite: the only prospect ahead was to finish driving.

It wasn't for the want of trying. I had put endless hours into writing letters and put endless bundles of hope into pillar-boxes. I had spent anxious mornings scanning the post for a reply that just might bring a glimmer of that hope back home with it, but all to no avail.

Eventually I gave up. As so often happens, that was the point at which the longed-for letter arrived.

Now, I certainly did *not* receive a letter saying 'Dear Mrs Smith, we would love to sponsor your husband for lots of money – immediately, if not sooner', with a resultant popping of champagne corks and general hysteria. What I *did* receive was a letter saying, 'Dear Mrs Smith, would your husband come and let us know a bit more about this carriage driving scene as we might just *possibly* be interested, if we thought it could work well for our company image.' It was the first sniff of interest we had had.

The company was 'John Carr' one of the largest joinery manufacturers in the country. A meeting was duly arranged and then there was nothing to do but wait. But I felt a tingling surge of hope that with one last enormous effort and a lot of luck we might yet reach the winning-post.

All of a sudden it was Christmas again. I arrived home having thankfully closed the office down for a whole glorious fortnight's holiday. I found everything was abnormally clean and tidy and cheery: not a dirty pot in sight, the carpet freshly hoovered and a cherry-red blaze roaring up the chimney of the stove. The clock ticked, the cats purred and there was an atmosphere of – anticipation.

On the table a bottle of wine stood open with two of our best glasses. In front of the wine, a single envelope. Not a Christmas card this one, elongated and with a paper window at the front: this was a business letter.

'Open it, Mum! Open it! Open it!' Megan clamoured, dragging the coat from my back and the bag from my hands.

My fingers trembled slightly as I removed a single piece of paper from the already opened envelope. Red, white and blue were the 'John Carr' colours; red, white and blue as the Union Jacks that were sewn so proudly on our horses' rugs. Red, white and blue were the hugs, the kisses the tears and the glorious – the indescribable – relief. In a heart-stopping driving finish we had come through from behind and pushed over that winning line just ahead in a race against time, bad luck and injury. Richard and the horses were now the 'John Carr Carriage Driving Team .

The next day, Christmas Eve, my first priority was to visit a wine shop and then the bank in Bishop Auckland. I had debt of faith to pay.

In the week before the previous Christmas, when all had

seemed utterly black – Richard with an unhealed leg, no job, no sponsor – and me only working on temporary contracts, I'd been quite prepared to throw the towel in on it all. It had taken a very far-sighted bank manager to see that *if* Richard's leg healed, and *if* we attracted another sponsor and *if* I found a full-time job, well, then everything could go on as before.

If we sold the horses, however, nothing would ever be the same again.

Two bottles of good quality champagne, a supply of plastic cups and a note that said quite simply 'We've done it!' were handed over to a totally astonished cashier. It was one of life's sweeter moments.

We celebrated by taking the pair out for a Christmas drive. We all clambered merrily aboard and, with horses adorned with tinsel on their browbands and bells on their harness pads, we set off, presenting a picture of seasonable jollity and high spirits.

Perhaps in our relief and excitement at what the coming year now held we got a little carried away. Perhaps we went just a little too far and a little too hard with horses that were, after all, not so very long back in work: they were certainly puffing and steaming a bit when we clattered up the back lane towards home to our awaiting mince pies and hot mulled wine. With the horses unhitched, unharnessed and rugged up to cool down, we consumed our Christmas fare with gusto, the horses licking sticky sweet mincemeat off our hands with equal delight.

The girls took the horses off for a walk down the lane to finish cooling. 'Do you think Bear is nodding a bit there?' I asked, almost casually.

'Well, actually, at a few points I didn't think Bear was quite level today when we were out. But then he seemed to be going all right again and I thought I must have been imagining it. Why? Do *you* think he's not level?'

'I'm not sure.' I answered truthfully, but the lovely warm and rosy glow that had so recently enclosed me was dispersing to be replaced with a tense and bitter chill. They say black coffee has a rapidly sobering effect; I know something that works even better. Worry.

'I think I'll just . . .'

'Hang on till they get back. Yes, I know,' Richard shook his head. 'You're worrying about nothing: he's probably just a little stiff and he's probably bruised his sole on a stone in the back lane. But I honestly don't think he's lame.'

Lame.

What an inadequate word 'lame' is: perhaps that's why people give 'lame' excuses.

It can mean that a horse has a scratch or a chip on its foot that makes it unwilling to put it down with full force, though little real damage has been done. Ponies become dreadfully lame through eating too much grass and developing laminitis when the delicate internal wall of the foot becomes inflamed. Tendons, ligaments, muscles can all be stretched, damaged or torn, leaving a horse more or less, temporarily or permanently, 'lame'. So slight may be the injury or the problem that it can take three vets watching a horse run up at an event two or three times before they can pronounce whether it is lame or sound. So terrible can lameness be when the horse 'breaks down' altogether, that the only solution can be a very final one.

Not being a vet, I could only watch intently as the returning horses picked their way up the back lane. He certainly seemed to be walking quite freely, and I didn't want him trotted up to get out of breath and sweaty again. Plonk, plonk, plonk, went his feet across the smooth concrete of the yard. If there was anything there, I was damned if I could see it. Perhaps, like Richard, I had been imagining it. It was probably only the uneven back street that had knocked him off balance.

I turned my mind from such neurotic thoughts. What if he *is* lame? I asked myself firmly. Dear Lord, he's been 'lame' in one form or another enough times in his nearly eighteen years. If he *was* lame, it certainly wasn't much.

Next day I was met by the heart-stopping sight of Karen leading Bear up the back street.

'He's lame, Mrs Smith.'

'Lame? Lame where? He's walking along quite level there.'

'It was when we started to trot, Mrs Smith,' she explained. 'As soon as we started to trot he was really nodding.'

'Which leg?'

'Nearside fore. I thought it best to get off and walk home.'

'Well, good girl for that, you did the best thing. Put the hosepipe on it for twenty minutes or so and put him in his box, well bedded up.'

It was not *much*, I kept telling myself, but somehow the worry had crept in, and it gnawed and nibbled incessantly at my peace of mind. After three days I had *no* peace of mind, admitted defeat and called the vet. We tried all the standard procedures, rest and cold water and gentle walking in hand. He was still as sound as a bell in walk, lame as a duck in trot and, most worrying of all, the swelling around the back of his lower front leg was now obviously visible and the heat easily detectable. Standing in made the heat and swelling worse. After gentle walking it reduced considerably. I didn't dare let him loose in the field, however, fearing he would fool around, chase the other horses and damage himself still further.

Trevor Hall confirmed my worst fears: it was a tendon injury. He also muttered darkly about suspensory ligaments and other bits and pieces that make up the intricate and marvellous mechanism that is a horse's leg. He administered all the standard procedures – anti-inflammatory powders to take daily and continuing with the cold hosing. My longed-for holiday lay in ruins and shambles. I don't think I actually celebrated New Year at all – it just happened.

The second week of my holiday developed a rhythm of its own. The day was punctuated by three 'walks out' in hand with exercise bandages on, and in between each walk Bear had a session with the cold hose.

It was the last day of my holiday. The first Sunday in January and a cold, grey, miserable day it was. A needle-sharp, thin rain fell intermittently. My early morning outing with Bear had been a miserable affair. Each morning I'd entered the box praying for a cool, smooth leg. Each morning I was greeted by a warm, puffy lump. The mid-day walk wasn't much more pleasant, though at least the leg wasn't as swollen as in the morning. I was doing my best to look after Bear myself, so as not to put extra work or responsibilities on to the girls, but I knew that the third and last walking out of the day would also be the last of my holiday. Back to work tomorrow. Then what? Would Richard or the girls diligently put the hose on and off his leg as I had done? Would they walk him out as a matter of priority?

I wrapped myself up both warmly and to be waterproof after glancing at the leaden, sullen sky that was already at 3.00 pm losing what little light it had afforded all day. I put Bear's New Zealand rug on so that he too would not get soaked if there were a deluge, and carefully wound the exercise bandages around his front legs. I was at the stage where I was winding bandages in my sleep.

'Come on, bonny lad,' I said, opening his door and pulling gently on the lead rein. As with any invalid, Bear was pathetically grateful for a change in his boring day and he followed readily out on to the yard. Down the back lane

we went and out on to the main street. It was completely
deserted, not even a stray dog or cat in sight. At 3.00
o'clock on a miserable January Sunday afternoon, the sensible residents of Stanley Crook were all sat in front of a
well banked fire. But lame horses and English women go
out in the January rain . . .

What was so damnably annoying, I thought as I trudged
along, was the even, rhythmic one-two-three-four of Bear's
feet as they plodded along beside mine. They sounded so
normal.

Yet he was not normal. I knew that if I were to increase
radically the pace of the walk he would begin to nod and
if I were to ask him to trot – which he would gladly do –
then his lameness would be evident for all to see. It was
going on too long: far too long. For nearly a fortnight now
he'd been hosed and rested and prescribed for by the vet
and yet there was not the slightest sign of improvement.
What injury? I had implored of Trevor Hall – what had he
actually done to himself?

There was, of course, no easy answer. The damage could
have been caused by something as stupid as getting up the
wrong way when lying down in his box, or injuring himself
while he was out in the fields, or simply accumulative
damage that had finally reached a crisis point. The cause
would remain a mystery. The effect was all too evident.
The final outcome – well, Trevor said gently, I might have
to consider that his competition days were finally over.

We plodded ever further from home this time. I wasn't
really leading him – Bear simply kept alongside me, the
rope quite slack in my hands. It's not fair, I wanted to
shout at the dilapidated pigeon crees, the garden sheds. It
couldn't, it simply *couldn't* end this way. Not for Bear. What
a paltry and insignificant thing to bring to a halt a career
that had spanned over a decade. All that muscle, all that
beauty, intelligence and ability – to be thrown on the scrap-
heap all because one tendon, or to be exact, about one

single inch of one tendon, was out of harmony with the rest of that marvellous body. He had battled – and won – over so many adversities of body and mind that to be defeated by something as simple as one inch of tendon was, somehow, an insult.

It's not *fair*, I raged inwardly on and on, the needle-sharp rain stinging my cheeks and mingling with the tears that flowed unchecked and unashamed. There must be something else we could do, I had implored Trevor, other drugs, other treatment. Well, the best treatment, of course, was the oldest and the cheapest, he'd replied, time and Mother Nature.

Now, where had I heard that before? Long ago. Another vet? Another injury – another battle. We *don't have* time I'd answered.

It was January – our new sponsors would want us on top form for the beginning of the season. Bear's deadline had to be Brighton in the first week of May. Mother Nature, Trevor had replied sagely, didn't work to deadlines. However . . . There were other treatments; radical new approaches to leg injuries. I could always call in a specialist – a 'leg man' – to have a look. It would be, he warned me, prohibitively expensive.

The coffers, I knew, were exhausted. New funds were coming, that was true, but they would be a little while yet in materializing and I simply couldn't ask the bank for any more elastic. So, for the moment, all I could do was to keep on walking, keep on hosing – and alternately curse and pray.

'We are *not*,' I told Bear defiantly as we rounded the last corner of the square we had just walked, 'we are *not* going to be defeated by this. Do you hear me? I will get you sound again – I don't care what it takes – I will get you sound.'

One, two, three, four, his metalled feet counted out on

the road. Counting the seconds, counting the passing of time.

Time was the commodity we were short of – more even than money. Time for the damage to repair slowly and thoroughly. Too few grains of sand left in the top of the hour-glass of the season to allow that to happen. Too many grains passed through and lying lost in the bottom of the hour-glass of his life. For the *real* problem with Bear's leg, the painful and unpalatable truth that lay at the heart of the problem, was quite simple. And I could rant and rage and cry at the elements all I wanted to to no effect: Bear was getting old.

The formalities surrounding the sponsorship with John Carr were finally completed. Almost reverently we gazed at the first cheque that arrived. However, Richard and I had slightly differing views on where priorities lay in how to allocate these funds. 'A new horse!' Richard repeated firmly.

A total silence hung between us for a minute before Richard said more kindly, 'Come on, Carol; face the facts. He's an old horse, he's had a charmed but very traumatic life. He's had ten solid years at the top of the sport, one way or another. But even he can't go on for ever.'

I felt the words like physical blows, blows that were all the more bitter because every word was true.

'If Bear is – out of action – what am I left with? Heather, a marvellous marathon horse, but she couldn't possibly do dressage; and I'm not really totally happy about Blizzard these days, he seems to be getting more and more uptight with every competition he does. He's only a little horse you know, and the sport is getting harder and harder. More and more demanding. I'm not sure he can cope anymore.'

This single, astonishing speech had decimated all my hopes and dreams for the coming season.

'So,' he pushed on still further, 'I need another horse, and not just *any* other horse; a very *special* other horse. One who knows his job thoroughly, one who is as versatile as Bear, able to do dressage and marathon equally well. Ideally I need two.'

'Isn't that a rather tall order?' I re-entered the debate caustically.

'I suppose it is, but I think I know where to begin looking.'

'I somehow thought you might.'

I realized I had sadly underestimated Richard recently. I'd been desperately trying to cling on to the past at any cost, he had been, quite rightly, looking to the future. 'What you say is quite right. It's just a bit hard to adjust to, that's all. It all sounds rather sort of . . . well, clinical, I suppose: like ordering spare parts.'

'Listen,' Richard said. 'It's change and survive or keep our heads in the sand and end up buried there. I know how we set away together – you and me, Bear and Blizzard – and it was wonderful, a marvellous combination that worked for a long time. But times change, horses change. *We've* changed. And we've all grown older. The goalposts are narrower now. There isn't just you and me to please anymore, we're not just amateurs anymore. Our new sponsors will expect, and must get, a totally professional team of people and horses so that we can give of our very best. Now, hard as it is for you to accept, that doesn't leave a lot of room for sentiment. To put it bluntly, we can't compete with horses that are verging on being geriatric or have a personality problem – no matter how much we love them.'

'May I ask where this new wonder horse is supposed to be lurking?' I was trying to keep the venomous sarcasm out of my voice, but the spoilt child in me had already made up its mind to detest this new creature – whoever it was.

'Mark Broadbent is selling his team of chestnut cobs. He's moved on into coaching and has a new team of bigger black horses. I've arranged to go down and see them and if I think there's one that is suitable, I will buy it. I've arranged to go on Tuesday.'

There was nothing much more to say. I couldn't possibly go, I would be at work. It would have to be Richard and one of the girls. Anyway, the last thing I would have any heart to do would be to help choose a successor to Bear.

'He lives in Devon, which is a hell of a drive, so I'll have to stay away overnight.'

'Fine,' I said, almost mechanically.

'Carol,' Richard said with a note of pleading in his voice, 'don't be like this: it's the way forward, the *only* way forward.'

'I'm not denying that. I just don't want to discard the present until I'm absolutely sure it is of no further use. I want one favour for Bear, if you'll allow it.'

'You don't have to beg favours for Bear, for God's sake!' Richard said uncomfortably.

'I want a further opinion on that leg while you're away. I'd like Mr Peart to look at it; he's an acknowledged "leg man". Bear deserves that at least.'

'Of course he does: now that we can afford it he deserves, and must have, the best treatment and every possible chance available. And I'll tell you something – I haven't written that old bugger off yet.'

I wished – Oh I desperately wished – that I could truly believe him.

The Leg-Man's opinion, after much probing and prodding, was that Bear was an old horse who had been through the wars but was still amazingly fit, overall. Perhaps, just perhaps, with fairly radical modern treatment, he could become sound again. Sound enough, anyway, to do dressage and obstacle driving. I would have to accept, however, that his marathon days were over.

'I can accept that, Mr Peart,' I told him honestly. 'I've always said that as long as there is a job for Bear to do he will be happy. To pension him off would be absolute cruelty; he loves to work. No, I'm sure he'll be happy to hang up his marathon harness a long as he still has a role to play.'

The treatment Mr Peart was proposing was called 'cold lasering'. He himself couldn't give the treatment: horses had to be sent to a lady in Cumbria who kept them at livery whilst she administered the laser three or four times a day and also saw to other therapeutic aspects such as a gentle exercise programme. The treatment was lengthy and expensive. A few quick mental calculations had resulted in the astounding fact that treatment for Bear would cost at least as much as he had cost me to buy him all those years ago. Fifteen years ago to be exact. Was it uneconomic, unrealistic or just plain unbalanced to justify spending all that money on an eighteen-year-old horse with a long and traumatic history behind him and perhaps not much of a future in front? Justifiable costs for a blood horse worth thousands or hundreds of thousands – but for a common old cob; a small hairy horse with thick legs?

I sat in my chair in front of the stove and felt the embrace of my home nourish and strengthen me. The gold lettering shone from the scores of red and blue and yellow rosettes that adorned the kitchen wall. A condensed testimony to eight years of gruelling hard work and determination. 'National Champion 1986 and 1987' they winked at me. 'Reserve National Champion 1989'. 'National Points League'; two seconds and two thirds (we'd never quite cracked that one championship, but we were getting closer every year). 'World Championships, Reisenbeck 1987', a magnificent multi-coloured rosette that showed that although we hadn't won anything, we had at least *been* there. And central to them all, beneath a large photo of Bear and Blizzard powering through the water hazard, the yellow rosette of the World Championships 1985. Beside it, on its five-coloured silk ribbon, a two-inch diameter circle of metal. A bronze World Championship Medal.

Justifiable costs for a common old cob? Damned right.

I sat up late into the evening listening for the unmistakable rumble that would herald the return of the horsebox. I suppose I had psyched myself up to be hostile, but when the ramp finally went down with a resounding thud, the emotion I felt most was sympathy for the bewildered, rather sweaty creature that had endured a very long journey quite alone in the enormous cavern of the box.

'He's called what?' I retorted when Richard answered my most obvious question.

'Hellfire,' he repeated, rather apologetically.

I watched the hairy apparition slither and stumble very inelegantly down the ramp, steaming gently in the chill night air.

'Hell's Bells,' I mumbled.

He was, Richard enthused, a fabulous horse. A wheeler out of Mark's team, which meant he was not afraid of hard pulling and, at nine years old, was just coming into his driving prime. His full title was 'Hengywm Hellfire'. He was a great work of biological engineering: massive shoulders, immense, powerful hindquarters and a great crested neck that had me swiftly checking his undercarriage to make sure it *was* a gelding that Richard had brought home.

Richard and the girls quickly retired to bed after their long journey and I offered to do late night stables.

Almost grudgingly I approached the box containing the new horse. From outside he appeared fatigued, bewildered and actually quite pathetic for a creature so well-built and manly. He was obviously delighted to see me, standing aside politely for me to enter. I just couldn't resist patting his muscled, crested neck and he nuzzled my hand when I extended it, before beginning to lick it with his warm, wet tongue. In fact, he was far more interested in my company than in the food I had brought him, so I took my leave of him to allow him to eat in peace. He followed me to the box door but did not try to barge out when I opened it. I had to admit he was a perfect gentleman in the stable.

'And,' I told him, receiving one last slobbery kiss on the hand, 'I suspect you are also just a big softy. Don't tell Richard – but I think you're rather nice.'

Next day, I tackled the issue of his name. Richard agreed he couldn't really yell 'Hellfire' as he attacked his hazards, so we swiftly agreed to shorten it to 'Fire'. An ironic choice, I thought afterwards, for a horse destined to replace one called 'Blaze'.

Conwy Blaze – or, more commonly, 'Bear' – received his hospital appointment the following day. Daphne Lane had a vacancy, David Peart phoned to say. She would take Bear just as quickly as Richard could get him there and felt that the sooner she started treatment the better.

I was disappointed and a little distraught at not being able to accompany him to Cumbria, but I had to work and if we put it off to the weekend, Daphne might have filled the vacancy. I fussed around as far as was possible, making sure he travelled in his best rug and took plenty of clean night clothes and bed socks with him. Before I left for work that morning I promised to visit him at the weekend.

I tended to avoid going on the yard that week because I found his empty box terribly unnerving, but I need not have worried about feeling out of touch with him: Daphne was on the phone most evenings.

For a lady I had never met, I soon liked her enormously. She was endlessly patient in explaining just what she hoped to achieve with her therapy, and always reassuring about Bear's general well being; he'd settled in very well; what a real character he was! Her grooms were but putty under his hooves.

Come the weekend, I followed the directions Richard had given me very carefully, but as the road dwindled and twisted more narrowly I began to think I was going to end up at a dead-end in the middle of nowhere on a Cumbrian hillside. Then I caught sight of the small sign I had been looking for beside a gate and a stone wall, and turned sharp right. A well-made farm drive took me across a couple of fields, down into a little valley, across a small stream and then twisted up towards a set of stone buildings. My curiosity tingled – what an unexpected and well-hidden habitation. The end of the drive passed a small outdoor arena where an extremely large and very high quality horse was tackling some mind-boggling jumps. I located a flat gravelled area that I took to be a car park and brought my Mini to a halt. Clutching a bag of carrots rather self-consciously, I set off to look for signs of life.

A low and ancient house snuggled into the Cumbrian hillside; its roof of heavily lichened slate dipped slightly like the back of an elderly horse, as though wearied by a long life of load-bearing, and the narrow, stone mullion windows looked out sleepily on to the yard. Around the side of the house I found a row of immaculate, red cedarwood boxes and from each an elegant, arrogant and obviously expensive head protruded. Except for the last box.

Hogged and workmanlike, a familiar close-clipped head with a white blaze turned in my direction – and gave no indication whatsoever of recognizing me.

'Bear!' I exclaimed ecstatically. He instantly withdrew into his box with an expression that plainly said 'Oh Lord, do *not* embarrass me in front of all these other horses.' I knew that expression well, it was exactly the same one that

Megan employed whenever I arrived to pick her up at a school friend's home.

'Bear?' I repeated in a more controlled and non-committal fashion. He consented to return to the front of the box – particularly when he eyed the bag of carrots.

'Can I help you?'

I turned to find a fresh faced girl in jodhpurs and rubber boots, a yard broom in one hand. 'Oh yes, sorry!' I apologized, acutely aware of my lack of courtesy. 'I couldn't see anyone around when I arrived, so I just came down here to see if I could find Bear. I'm his owner, Carol Smith.'

Her face relaxed into a broad beam of pleasure. 'Of course, Daphne said you were coming today. Even out here in the sticks you can never be too careful. Some very suspicious types around – particularly near the racehorses!

'Daphne's down at the out-door school; they've been working with a young showjumper. I'll pop down and tell her you're here.'

'Please don't disturb her – I'm happy to stay with Bear until she's finished.'

'They were just finishing the lesson off when I left,' she assured me. 'It's no trouble.'

'And Bear? Has he been causing any trouble with all these large strangers around?'

'Bear!' she retorted, quite shocked. 'He's an old sweetheart, aren't you sunshine?'

Bear smirked visibly in his five-star luxury box that obviously came complete with doting room service. I hope it's not too long before you come home, my lad, I thought to myself, or Stanley Crook is going to be an awful comedown from this.

The girl swung off down an immaculately tended path with carefully landscaped shrubbery on each side. An overhanging roof ran the length of the stable block, allowing the horses to gaze out of their boxes without the inconvenience or discomfort of getting wet on rainy days. A neatly carpentered saddle rack stood at the side of each stable door, and I sat down on Bear's to enjoy his view. And what a view it was across the little valley and on to the opposite hillside. What a peaceful and very beautiful place this really was. A far cry from Stanley Crook.

A person of middle height was striding vigorously up the path to the stable. She smiled broadly and offered me a hand that obviously worked very hard for its living.

'Carol? I'm Daphne. Glad to meet you at last.' She had a wonderful face: alive, strong, impossible to age. Curly, slightly wayward hair was piled roughly into a pony-tail on top of her head. Her clothes, like herself, conveyed 'comfortable'. I knew, without any further word exchanged, that I had just met a remarkable person, an exceptional person. I also knew that if there was anyone who could sort out Bear's injured and work-worn leg, that person stood there before me.

'I don't have to ask you how he is,' I smiled. 'He's obviously made himself quite at home and is plainly thoroughly enjoying himself. How has his treatment come on in the last day or two though?'

'Well, let's go in and I'll show you.'

Daphne opened the box and Bear respectfully stood aside. He obviously admired this lady as well. She swiftly unwound the stable bandages from Bear's front legs and began to feel them carefully.

'A lot of the adhesions are breaking down already, which is wonderful. The fluid in the joint is less noticeable as well, but I think we've still got a ways to go with the actual tendon. Here, feel.'

She placed my hand under her own broad, strong one, pressing my fingers down at appropriate places. Straightening up she gave Bear a hearty pat on the neck.

'You're doing well, aren't you Bear?' she spoke confidently to him.

'Do you think,' I asked, my confidence wavering for the

first time, 'that he stands a chance of recovery? Completely I mean – well, I mean enough so that he can compete at least at dressage level again?'

'David Peart has told me about his past history – and his present glories – and I do understand how important he is to you for this forthcoming season with his new sponsor.'

'Oh, it's more than that. It's important for Bear himself – and of course for me. He's probably just a very ordinary sort of little cob compared to the blood horses you have here, but to me . . . to me . . . Bear is irreplaceable. He's my "number one" you see, my first horse, my *own* horse – we've reached the heights together and been down to the other place a few times as well. This leg is so . . . *petty*, so trivial, compared with what he's been through. Yet it's the single thing threatening to change or even end the life he knows and loves.'

It all burst out of me, I really hadn't meant it to, but when it had there was a thoughtful, measured silence as all I had said was digested carefully by the strong, compassionate woman who stood beside Bear. 'Of course,' I added quietly, 'I'm not so foolish as to think he can go on for ever. The years are bound to catch him up eventually. It's just that I had always thought . . . you won't laugh at me for this will you?'

She shook her head with complete sincerity.

'I always thought that he would *tell* me when he had had enough of the driving world; when he was ready to take it easy and eat daisies and go for the occasional little hack. I just don't feel he's ready to give up yet.'

'How old is he exactly?'

'He'll have his eighteenth birthday in a couple of months' time. I've always threatened to give him a cake and the key to the stable.'

'Don't forget to ask me to the party,' said Daphne. There was disarming sincerity in her voice.

She carefully replaced the bandages on his legs then said, 'Come on, up to the house. I'll show you something.'

The house was as comfortable and untidy as Daphne herself. It was indeed an ancient house, with massive oak beams, thick walls and cosy-sized rooms that warmed easily. The long narrow kitchen overflowed with a mixed-marriage of domestic, culinary and equestrian equipment. Daphne moved a few cats, the odd pan of barley and linseed, to clear enough space to make a couple of cups of tea. We then went through into the sitting-room which also overflowed, this time mainly with rosettes, dozens of framed photos of horses doing just about everything it's possible for horses to do, and a thousand back issues of *Horse and Hound*. The whole house was impregnated with the smell of leather, saddle-soap and woodsmoke from the stove. It was quite wonderful.

Daphne carefully removed one photo from amongst the many. She gazed at it thoughtfully for a moment before passing it to me.

'Look at her.'

A handsome, dark brown mare, well made and with an intelligent, kind face stared at me. Daphne was astride her and, from the surrounding mêlée of horses and hounds, it was not hard to identify the scene as a hunting meet.

'She's lovely,' I answered truthfully. 'What a wise face.'

'How old?' demanded Daphne.

'Oh, it's a very hard one: I mean she could be almost any age just looking at her there. She's obviously not a gangly youngster but her back is level and she's very fit and well-muscled.' I suspected Daphne might be trying to pull a sneaky trick on me; trying to make some comparisons to cheer me. 'She wouldn't be eighteen by any chance, would she?'

'No, she wouldn't. She's thirty-one in that photo.'

'Thirty-one!' I gazed hard and believed it less.

'Honestly, yes, thirty-one. Still hunting – not ridiculously hard, of course, but still in love with it and life in general.'

'Is she still . . .'

'No,' Daphne said softly, gently taking the photo from me and replacing it. 'She had to be put down two years after that photo. A stupid accident in the field – she got really badly kicked by a youngster, right behind the knee. There was nothing even I could do.

'Have you finished your tea?' I nodded and put my cup down. 'Then I'd like to show you something else.'

We went back out of the house and down the bankside that sloped away from it towards the little stream that ran in the valley bottom. Facing us, the hillside was pure Cumbrian fellside, like the rest of the surrounding fields. Sheep grazed on poor and, at this time of the year, withered grass and not a bush or tree relieved the landscape. Only grey grass, grey sheep and grey stone walls. Where the bankside began to drop more steeply towards the stream, Daphne opened a little gate in a stout wooden fence and we walked into . . . a garden. My head could not accept what my eyes saw. A generous green, even in this most lifeless time of year, the grass was short and springy under my feet. Many of the trees were leafless, as befitted the season, but many of the shrubs were green and even in its winter, skeletal form the effect was quite breathtaking.

At the bottom of the slope the stream ran over little waterfalls, so wonderfully built with large natural boulders that they looked as if they'd been there since the first week of creation. The empty fingers of weeping willows trailed gently in the water. A hopeful gaggle of mallard, swimming in the pool at the base of the waterfall, scrabbled out of the water and headed for Daphne, chattering softly. She dug in her pockets and found a few crumbled horse cubes which she scattered on the grass for them.

'It's beautiful.' It was an inadequate thing to say.

'My husband Donald spent twenty years creating this

garden,' she told me, leading me over to a sturdy wooden bench. 'They said it couldn't be done. The locals thought he was mad. But he had a theory that there was just enough shelter under the lee of the hill in this spot to allow things to grow and to survive the winter. The waterfall and the stream – that was just a sheep crossing there; all paddled mud. It took a long time to persuade the farmer to sell it to us, but I think Donald just wore him down eventually. And now it is . . . our refuge, a place of calm in a frantic world. You must see it in the spring!' she insisted. 'Knee deep in daffodils!

'But this is not what I really brought you to see.'

She led the way along the stream bank a little and then up towards the crest of the hill again. Beneath a large laurel bush stood a neatly carved headstone.

Daphne gazed at the inscription quietly for a while before saying, 'Odd sort of name for a mare, "Mrs Bag-shot", but we all just called her "June". She was my "only one" as well. She certainly wasn't my first horse, I've had horses of my own before and since, dozens of them over my lifetime. But she was . . . very special. The only one there'll ever be quite like her for me. Thirty years is a very long time together. So you see,' she turned her warm, very level gaze towards me, 'I *do* understand about Bear and what he means to you. And I might add that there really *is* something special about him – we've all sensed that here. The girls think he's wonderful.'

I smiled gratefully. 'I was so worried that he would be out of place here – inferior somehow to all the expensive thoroughbreds.'

Daphne gave a derisory snort. 'I don't judge a horse by the amount on its price tag. There have been horses through here worth a small fortune, but I wouldn't have given tuppence for them. Others, well, they're priceless. Just as Bear is to you.'

We wandered slowly back up the slope, leaving the tranquillity of the garden, back to the bustle of the yard where feeding was in progress for the row of impatient guests.

Daphne glanced at her watch. 'Lord, is that the time! Right, I've got another treatment to do for Bear and then he gets bandaged up and walked. You can stay and watch if you like – and take him for his exercise after if you want to – if you have time that is.'

I stayed and did both of those things. It was fascinating to watch Daphne seated beside Bear's foreleg with her 'laser'. There were no dramatic science fiction-type sights and sounds, no sizzling, crackling, ruby beams. Just an attachment that led from a box-like apparatus that had a multitude of dials and knobs. Daphne moved this attachment slowly and carefully across Bear's injured leg, constantly checking and adjusting the position she used. The process took about twenty minutes.

Afterwards, Bear was bandaged and I was given instructions as to where to walk him so as to keep to relatively level ground. He was certainly on his mettle compared with when he left home. No ambling along beside me this time: he strode eagerly along the road, almost hauling me behind him, and once or twice I had to check him with the lead rope to prevent him setting off at a jog.

I drove home more content than I'd been in weeks, knowing that without any doubt Bear's welfare, and his future, lay in the right hands. A very remarkable pair of hands.

After a total of two and a half weeks Bear came home. I wasn't to delude myself that he was back to normal. The laser had freed the adhesions, reduced the inflammation and promoted a healthy blood supply that had speeded up healing. Now the tendon needed time to consolidate the work that had been done on it: time to settle down again, time to harden off. Bear was still to be kept inside, walked out at least three times a day and then have a special 'frozen' bandage put on the leg when he returned from walking out. No trotting, no fooling around. Just steady walking for a few weeks.

Bear had other ideas. It was, after all, almost two months since the injury had first manifested itself. Two months since he had last done anything interesting. Two months since he'd last been out loose in a field. Bear was absolutely fed up.

It was impossible to take him for his walk in hand with just a headcollar on, he would pull you off your feet and not take any notice of where you wanted to go. He had to be taken out with a bit and bridle on, so that there was some element of steering and control. During the week, with the dark nights, I couldn't walk him at all, it all had to be done during the day whilst I was at work. Lesley soon announced that she didn't feel safe out with him and so the task fell to Karen three times a day. As the days ticked by, she reported that even she was having more and more difficulty with him and so, come the weekend, I took him out myself to find out what was going on. He was awful.

He trembled and jumped at every mortal thing we passed. A paper bag on the ground suddenly became a white elephant and he would shoot past it. To make him *walk* was nearly impossible, he jigged and joggled on the spot and if I got cross with him and yanked on his bridle he would come to a halt for a moment or two and then, ears back and eyes rolling, surge forward again. Seeing a patch of grass he fancied, he simply hauled me across the road – me heaving and yelling and swearing – he taking not the blindest bit of notice. I began to worry as to whether I would get him – or myself – back home in one piece.

'He's dreadful!' I told Richard. 'I've honestly never known him like this, *never*! What on earth are we going to do?'

'I'll take him out this afternoon,' said Richard grimly. 'I'll sort the old so and so out.'

Though they were both sweaty, it was Richard that was limping when they got back.

That night we lay in bed and listened to an incessant imperious banging from Bear's stable. On and on he went, banging his forefoot against the bottom door in impatience. In the end I staggered out in my dressing-gown and wellies and closed his top door firmly in his face. 'I've had enough of this my lad,' I told him. 'What on earth do you think that'll be doing to your foreleg, eh?'

In retaliation he began pawing the concrete of his floor instead.

Next morning I phoned Daphne. 'I think he's gone over the top,' I told her anxiously. 'He's just stopped listening to anything that we're trying to tell him, or do to him for his own good. It's as if he's got one single thought in his brain – "I want to be OUT!" '

'It does happen,' Daphne told me. 'That's why it's sometimes kinder to destroy a horse with a really bad leg injury rather than to try and nurse it in a confined space for a long while. He sees the others going out on exercise or out in the field and he's shut in a box. He wants space and freedom and grass, not a box and a bridle and hay.'

'What are we going to do?' I wailed.

'Let him have what he wants,' Daphne answered simply.

'What! Won't that be dangerous?'

'It's a risk, yes. But in a way, he must be feeling well enough on that leg to want to jog and trot on it, and if he's bashing the door down and digging up the concrete through the night, that's every bit as risky for the tendon. Take all the other horses out of the field, put support bandages on both front legs and turn him out.

'Then pray. The first ten minutes will be the most hair-raising and crucial, till he gets all that pent up frustration out of his system. After that, well, he should settle down and graze, and then you can just leave him to stay out all day. Put the ice bandages on when he comes back in. Don't be alarmed if there's some swelling when he comes in at night for the first day or two – there's bound to be some reaction. But if he's grossly inflamed or obviously lame, phone me at once and I'll bring the laser over there.'

'Oh Daphne, thank you so much. I just didn't know what to do for the best.'

'Well I'd have preferred it if we'd got another week or so behind him before we turned him out, but sometimes, you know, the horse is his own best judge of when he's ready.'

'Short of waving a placard out of his stable, I don't think he could be more emphatic at the moment. He wants *out*.'

'Keep me informed.'

'I will,' I assured her.

Richard had grave doubts. 'I think you're mad,' he told me bluntly. 'All this time, all the trouble – not to mention the expense – and you're just going to blow it all by letting him out there to rip that tendon to pieces.'

'I hear what you're saying,' I told him unhappily, 'but Bear is going out of his mind. He's getting too dangerous to take out in hand. Dangerous to himself and dangerous to the girls. He *won't* walk anyway, which is the object of the exercise, and he's just pacing and banging in his stable all day which is hardly good for the leg, is it?'

'True,' Richard admitted.

'So, short of trussing him up like a turkey and giving him an armed escort, how do we exercise him? Exercise is an important part of his treatment. And . . .' I needed so hard to convince myself that what I was doing was right, that I was deliberately working myself up '. . . healing isn't just a mechanical process, something that just happens to the body. If he's not in a content, happy frame of mind, he isn't going to get any better anyway. And . . .' I took another breath, '. . . if he keeps on like this much longer, he could end up sound in his leg but out of his mind!'

At this point Richard did a Pontius Pilate on me. 'He's your horse,' he said simply, and walked away.

It was difficult to bandage a horse that was fidgeting and twitching all the time, but Karen and I managed somehow and I checked the bandages for the umpteenth time before I allowed her to open the stable door. Bear surged out, dragging me beside him.

'Oh you stupid, cantankerous old animal!' I flung at him in despair.

Karen went to open the door that led to the field and I had great difficulty in getting him to stop long enough to get his lead rein off. My heart was going like a trip hammer and my stomach felt like the automatic washer on spin.

'For God's sake, Bear, be *careful!*' I told him as I slipped the clasp.

He was gone. His first act of freedom was a display of bucking. Up in the air, up with his back, out with his legs. And again. And again. Like a stupid two-year-old.

Then he stopped dead still, tail raised like a banner, neck back and nostrils dilated. He screamed a defiant whinny like a stallion across his domain and then he began to run.

Footsteps behind me at the gate told me that Richard hadn't, after all, been able to stay away. I had expected Bear to snort and cavort and prance round a bit. Give the odd buck and even have a little canter. I had not expected this. He tore around the field at a flat out gallop. Like a creature demented, he headed straight for the fence and for one awful, heart-stopping moment, I thought he was going to lift, jump and be gone over the horizon. Instead, which was equally awful, he slammed his brakes on yards from the bottom of the fence and, front legs stretched in front of him, slithered and skidded across the wet muddy ground to a juddering halt. Then he turned round and set off to gallop in the other direction.

'There goes your tendon,' Richard flung at me and, shaking his head, retreated to his workshop.

It was a long and awful day. There was no question of catching Bear; any approach within fifty yards sent him clattering off at a gallop. I knew him too well of old. I knew he would come in when he was good and ready. We turned all the other horses out – there were surely no further risks to be taken even if they did chase each other around.

Actually, the presence of his companion cobs was what seemed to finally settle Bear, and by early afternoon they were grazing together as a group.

At teatime, when we banged the feed bucket on the gate in the ritual 'time to come in' message, Bear was there in his usual place in the queue. He came in and went to his bed as quietly as a lamb. One-two-three-four, his feet sounded level and sure across the yard. With trembling hands Karen and I stripped off the bandages and I ran my hand down his near-side foreleg. Slightly warm, slightly swollen, but nothing radical – not yet anyway. Muttering prayers and invocations, I put on his ice bandage for fifteen minutes and then bandaged normally for the night. There was nothing to do but wait for the morning.

I agonized over the decision all over again as I lay in bed that night. What other choice had there been? I couldn't have kept him penned up in the stable much longer.

'Is he all right do you think?' Richard mumbled in a voice that was supposed to sound noncommittal, but which only proved that he was thinking about him too.

'I won't really know till the morning. I can only hope and pray that what Daphne said was right – sometimes the horse itself knows best what's good for it. Knows when it's recovered enough to do something more strenuous. Bear knew the last time; I only hope he's right this time.'

'What do you mean last time?'

'After his accident in the septic tank. He was supposed to take things very easy for a whole year, but one day, after about six months, he suddenly went crackers in the field. Bucked and reared and galloped like a creature demented. Just like today.

'I rang the vet and told him Bear had just told me he was recovered and the vet wouldn't believe me. I pointed out that if Bear did have a dicky ticker and damaged lungs, he would have dropped stone dead carrying on like that. The vet came out and examined him and he went back into gentle work the next day.'

'Carol, you've lost me – and I would like to get to sleep!'

'All I'm saying is that perhaps, just perhaps, Bear's trying to tell us he's really on the mend and he wants to go back into action again.'

'And perhaps he's just an impatient, cantankerous, stubborn so and so. Just like his owner. Good night!'

There was not a single bang from the stable that night.

'Take it very steady for the next couple of weeks: walk riding only. Use exercise bandages – and use your common sense as to when to push him any further or harder.' David Peart stood up and ran his hand down Bear's neck. 'I'm glad he's come through. Daphne took a real shine to this one. Marvellous thing that laser, marvellous.'

'Marvellous lady that used it,' I corrected him. 'Healing can't come from a machine alone: it comes through the hands – from the heart.'

'Good luck with him,' David said as he left me with Bear in the stable.

'That's the one thing Bear has always had,' I assured him.

'And what contrasting colour would you like the icing?'

'Pardon?'

'The icing on the cake. What colour would you like the icing?'

'Oh! Would it be possible to have it brown?'

'Brown! Oh, that is unusual. We normally get asked for

pink or blue. You know – pink for girl, blue for boy. Is it
for a boy or a girl by the way?'

'Actually, it's for a horse.'

The lady in the baker's shop rocked visibly and then
eyed me as if I was some sort of hoaxer. 'A horse! You
want a birthday cake for a *horse*?'

'That's right,' I reassured her, 'and not just any old birthday cake – an *eighteenth* birthday cake.'

'Right,' she said, smoothing her overall down and picking up her pen and book, as if she took orders for horses'
birthday cakes every day of the week. 'You'd like a twelve
inch square model, sponge filling . . .'

'. . . seeing as you don't do carrot cake,' I muttered
quietly.

'What was that?'

'Oh, nothing. Do carry on.'

'. . . sponge filling. And a message?'

'Message? Ah yes. I think "Happy Eighteenth Birthday,
Bear" would do splendidly.'

'Happy Eighteenth . . .' she began writing laboriously in
her book. 'Did you say *Bear*? Hang on, I thought you said
this was for a *horse*?' She was eyeing me very suspiciously
now.

'Bear,' I explained patiently, for what felt to be the milli-
onth time in my life, 'is the name of the horse – his nick-
name, if you like.'

'We'll need a deposit,' she said firmly. She was obviously
worried about being left with a fraudulent cake on her
hands.

'I'll pay the full amount now gladly,' I told her, extracting
my cheque book from my bag.

'Oh,' she said, relaxing visibly. 'That'll be fine.'

I suppose it didn't matter what fool nonsense people put
on their cakes, as long as they paid for them.

'And decorations? For an Eighteenth – how about some
small silver keys?'

'That would be lovely – and I think some silver horse-shoes would just finish it off nicely.'

'Plus silver horseshoes,' she wrote in large letters in her book and smiled sweetly. 'Ready for Saturday morning.'

He wore his very impressive rug, complete with Union Jack of course.

Hellfire nearly went through the roof when the corks went pop, but Bear never batted an eyelid. All the past and present girl grooms that we could muster had arrived, and each one had brought a card, rows of which now hung along the front of Bear's stable.

It felt quite decadent swigging champagne – the real stuff, the best – at midday and consuming chunks of sweet sticky cake. It had been a shame to cut into it actually: a real triumph of the confectioner's art in white, silver . . . and brown.

I laid on a sort of running buffet in the stable and the cobs all got a special midday feed, well-laced with chopped carrot and apple. They finished off with chunks of cake, the sweet, sticky fondant icing particularly delighting them as it stuck to their teeth. Blizzard discovered a penchant for champagne, curling his front lip nearly over his nose in ecstasy. It was a great party.

Only one tiny disappointment lurked in the corner of my heart: I'd organized it all very properly and officially with real invitations going out, but only one had remained unanswered and only one person had not managed to turn up. Still, it was a very long way from Cumbria.

The cake was a sad and crumbled ruin of its former glory and the champagne all but gone when there was a sound of banging car doors and a quick, firm tread up the yard.

'Am I too late?' came a voice from behind a large sack tied with a big red ribbon.

'Daphne!' I cried. She dumped her sack and gave me a big hug. 'You made it!'

'This is one party I wouldn't miss for the world. But what a place to live at! "Stanley Crook". My God, I think I would have found Afghanistan easier!'

She swept her gaze round our small, very modest yard. The breeze-block and tin shed stables, peeling paint on the doors. I thought of cedar-wood boxes, Cumbrian fells and landscaped waterfalls, and wilted inside.

Daphne's smile betraying nothing – except perhaps understanding.

'So, where is he then? The birthday boy?'

'In here,' I told her happily, 'and he's fine Daphne, really fine. Riding out with the others, driving single, driving in the pair. Just dressage of course, no hazards and no long hard road work. We feel so blessed to have him sound again that we don't want to push our luck.'

'Give him one of these to be going on with and I'll just get something else from the car.' Daphne pointed to the sack on the ground tied with ribbon and set off back to the car.

I undid the bow to reveal a mountain of best carrots, large and clean and juicy.

'Oh, Daphne!' I chuckled.

She returned with a bag from which she produced an enormous birthday card adorned with cut-out photos of Bear when he was over in Cumbria, then a huge pink rosette. It had obviously been especially made: of all the dozens of rosettes that adorned our house and harness room we'd never been awarded one that pronounced in large bold letters on its dangling ribbons 'Eighteen'. Normally rosettes weren't awarded below sixth place. But then this one also declared on its oval face 'Happy Birthday, Bear'.

'How did you manage that?' I asked, astonished.

'I had it made!'

'Oh my goodness! Quick, come on or there'll be nothing left!'

Rosette proudly pinned to his headcollar, Bear remained the centrepiece of his party until the last drop and the last crumb had been consumed.

After one final carrot, the rest were stored safely in the feed room before we had an epidemic of belly ache.

I proudly introduced Daphne to the other cobs and she had a word of admiration for Blizzard and Heather. When she came to Hellfire, however, she paused longer and gazed harder.

'He's magnificently put together, Carol – look at the legs on him; and those shoulders, that chest, that neck! He seems to have a lovely nature, too. I haven't seen him move of course, but just by looking at him I would say if you're looking for a worthy successor to Bear, you couldn't do better than this animal. How old is he?'

'He's nine,' I informed her.

'Then he's got it all before him, hasn't he? His time is yet to come.'

It was a prophetic note for the party to end on. But, as with the prophecies of the oracle of old, it had a double meaning. Hellfire's time was indeed to come, but not, as we might so naturally have assumed, with us. Nothing we had perhaps blithely imagined and planned for the future, that afternoon in the stable yard, was to actually materialize. Oh, it was undoubtedly a new beginning that day, poised on the brink of a new season, of new sponsorship. But it was to be the beginning of the end.

15

Legacy

The horsebox was old, but serviceable. However, 'Church Hill', rising out of the very centre of the little market town of Crook, was exceptionally steep. So steep that it was the hill chosen for the 'ultimate test' of fitness prior to a competition. If the horses could set away at a spanking trot in Crook market-place and keep that pace, never slacking, up the gruelling gradient of Church Hill right to the very top, without puffing and blowing excessively, then they could cope with anything a marathon demanded of them.

The horsebox, gears grinding and straining, crawled away up the last part of the hill at a speed that would have been derisory to the cobs. It slowly withdrew even further from my sight, though I couldn't make myself look away until it had totally disappeared over the horizon that September afternoon in 1992. Finally, I had to turn my eyes elsewhere, and the unavoidable direction was down, to look at the lead rope that lay loosely coiled in my hands. I had steeled myself for days against this moment, talked common sense to myself in my sleep, but my emotional preparations were, as I had known all along, a totally inadequate defence against the reality of that moment.

Bear had gone.

I stood there in the silence of the little riding stable yard, aching and empty and feeling, above all else, disbelief that I had actually found the courage to do it. For eighteen years Bear had been my responsibility. My pride, my joy – my friend.

His hoof-beats had rung out the rhythm of almost half my life. But in the past two years that rhythm had changed so much and so swiftly that it had become painfully obvious that our lives were no longer in unison, that I could no longer provide him with what he was used to, with what he needed to make his life worthwhile.

The one thing I was very sure of and which helped me cling to the rightness of my decision to let Bear go was that, at rising twenty-one years of age, he still had a great deal to give that was worthwhile. I knew that leaving me that day marked a new beginning for him, even if it felt like the end to me. His new life would be very different and no doubt strange at first, but one that would be enjoyable and rewarding. At the end of a long and illustrious life in which he had had so many starring roles, Bear had just made his final career move. Oh, he was still 'mine', technically. I was still his registered owner and he could never be moved on from his new home without my consent. But the responsibility for him, for his welfare, for his work, for his day-to-day life was now out of my hands. That now lay with the Strang Riding Centre for the Disabled at Washington, some twenty-five miles away.

That was where Bear now truly belonged.

I set off slowly and rather unsteadily towards the little stable that Bear had occupied for the last year or so, my practical common sense conscience telling me to get on with it and not prolong the agony of setting it all fair and getting away from there one last time. I knew what I had done was right for Bear. Absolutely, without any doubt I knew. But for myself? I started to sort the clean and dirty straw with a fork in what was, after all the years, a reflex action. This time, this last time, I found myself sluggish and uncoordinated. I paused to pick up his old stable rug, lying in the corner when I had stripped it that morning. It was dropping to bits. Darned and mended endless times; patched with bits of sack and canvas. There were even, I noticed as I folded it automatically in half then half again, patches on patches. It was so tatty that I'd felt too ashamed to send it with him to his new home. I'd bought a new one for him and the driver had put it carefully in the front of the horsebox, still in its polythene bag; stiff as a board and probably about as comfortable. Bear would no doubt curse me that night and wonder where his scruffy but softly comfortable nightwear had gone.

At that thought I hugged the old rug closer to me and the oh so familiar smell of hessian and wool and sweet hay and horse enveloped and then overcame me. I sank onto the pile of straw I had just so recently carefully piled up and buried my face to weep into the rough comfort of the rug. It was my last link with a way of life I would never know again. For Bear's departure that day was the more poignant for being the last departure. He was the final one; now they were all gone.

The problem with pinnacles is that you cannot cling onto them forever. Fatigue and gravity take over and then the only way is down. The upward journey, however arduous, is at least forward movement. We – horses and people alike – had achieved impossible heights; we had clawed our way up from nothing to the very top of an international sport. It had taken a decade, but we had made it. We had all suffered and changed and aged along the way – but we had made it. Getting to the top had required love, mutual support, determination and, perhaps most important, a sense of humour. Staying at the top required, I discovered, an altogether colder and more brutal approach.

The season of 1990 had been, in many ways, successful. Bear's injury healed sufficiently for him to compete in dressage, but he was nevertheless 'phased out' of the team to be replaced by a younger ex-team mate of Hellfire's called Harry. Blizzard, Richard had insisted on selling, and although he went to a good private home, his unhappy face the day he was taken away will always haunt me. He was still uttering shrill whinnies of protest as the trailer disappeared down Stanley front street. I ached for days. Heather put in a good season as a marathon horse but even her future came under scrutiny when thoughts turned to the next season. Was she too old? Was she versatile enough? Hellfire lived up to all expectations, proving himself almost unbeatable on marathons. By the end of the season the horses had achieved the one national honour that had previously eluded them, the National Points League Championship.

But, throughout the year, slowly and inexorably, Richard and I slipped apart. I was no longer needed – or indeed felt wanted – at events, except as a 'hostess' to conduct small talk with the guests. The new sponsorship provided new horses, a professional but impersonal staff, a shiny but impersonal horsebox and a show schedule that took the whole lot away from Stanley, from me and Megan for weeks on end. The only issue became 'Did they win?' and if not, why not? It was all hollow, false, meaningless to me. Success – predictable, reliable, almost monotonous success – had been bought, but at a terrible price. Richard and I had always been an unlikely combination and our relationship had been founded on 'going along the road together' to see what we could achieve with a motley assortment of equipment and a pair of horses that were special because of their determination and character, not their price tag. We had, realistically, little else in common. With Blizzard sold, Bear retired and Heather under scrutiny, I found there was nothing left but a devastating vacuum. Nearly a decade of daily focusing my life and heart on the needs of the horses and fighting for their survival was over.

Richard and I parted our ways.

The new, big horses continued their driving career, Heather was retired to a wonderful home with my cousin, Pauline, in the Midlands and Bear, of course, stayed with me. It was not the way I imagined it would have ended, it was not the way I would have wanted it to have ended – but then endings seldom are.

The circle of my life came round in full as I found myself responsible once more only for my daughter and that old war horse, Bear. It was a prospect that did not alarm or distress me: it was one I actually took pleasure and great comfort in, sharing my life with the two beings who meant the most to me. Megan was now a young lady of thirteen. I had perhaps five years before she left for college and probably left home, full-time, for good. I wanted, needed, to make up to her for the many times I felt I had given the demands of the horses first priority. Megan had simply had to fit in. And she always had – uncomplaining, understanding, she had fitted in. It was all the more humbling because she didn't even like horses. Well, now it was time *she* took priority.

And Bear? Well, I had wanted to catch up on many lost years with him as well. Years of simple pleasures; of gentle hacks and quiet drives down leafy lanes. Of going out with him because I felt like it, or because it was a lovely day – not because his training schedule demanded he be trotted for twelve kilometres. Time to enjoy each other again.

With the sale of the farm, my main problem became where Bear was to live. Suitable accommodation for Megan and me was easily found and we moved into a small, pretty cottage in Crook. Accommodation for a horse was another matter as for the first time in many years I had neither stable nor paddock to call my own. I was, thank God, reasonably financially secure. In 1990 a full-time lecturing job had become vacant at Peterlee College in the School of Special Needs and, to my immense joy, I succeeded in getting the post. Ironically, that move back to a full-time professional teaching career, a job that was not just a means of creating money but rather a committed and deeply rewarding way of life, had driven the wedge between Richard and me even deeper.

My financial situation was not so generous, however, that I could afford to keep Bear in the manner to which he was accustomed, with a personal groom to devote an entire day to his grooming, exercise and general well-being. Keeping a horse at livery to those standards was well beyond my reach. In the end I had to settle for a very modest establishment in Crook where I knew his basic welfare requirements would be provided during the week and where I hoped I could make up any deficiencies at the weekends. So it was that a horse whose days had been structured and demanding for the last eighteen years, suddenly found himself turned out into a field in the morning to stand idle all day, till it was time to put him back in the stable at night. As for many humans plunged suddenly into premature retirement, the change was not a healthy one. Oh, I tried my best at weekends to cheer him up and do interesting things with him, but I knew in my heart I wasn't filling the vacuum that had developed in his life. He became lethargic and dispirited. His 'spark', which had sustained him through so much, seemed to burn ever lower. I watched him grow old before my eyes as the months passed, and agonized over what I could do to halt the deterioration. It was not a physical deterioration in any great sense, though his joints perhaps took a little longer to loosen up at the start of a ride. At twenty-one years of age Bear was still phenomenally well and fit, his muscles hardened by all those years of work and sound in wind and limb. It was the loss of identity, of familiar companions and, above all, of purpose that seemed to afflict Bear. I knew that he still had so much to give that was worthwhile. So much experience and talent to share. But with whom? And how?

The only achievement of that final season of 1990 that had not been hollow to me was when Bear had been tested by the Riding for the Disabled Association to be used as a driving horse. Until that time, there had been a height restriction of thirteen hands, two inches on horses for Driving for the Disabled, but as soon as this restriction was lifted I had submitted Bear for the test and he had passed with flying colours. I then dreamt of being able to at last provide Heather Stoddart with the combination she so desperately desired in her driving – power, speed and safety. The collapse of my known world had swept all those dreams away with it however. Without the farm there was now no base for me to run the Group from. Little Bobby Dazzler, also rendered homeless in the upheaval, was moved by George to a farm not far away, where he tragically fell victim to a local tetanus epidemic. With Bobby's death I really felt that all my efforts and involvements with horses and the disabled were over for ever. But as God firmly shut the door on Stanley Crook, a new door at Peterlee was slowly creaking open.

My job at Peterlee involved working with students with a wide range of disabilities and learning difficulties. The course I taught on, 'Bridging', aimed to encourage these students' personal and vocational development in all possible ways. Very often, improving self-esteem and self-discipline were the keystones to real progress. The College encouraged any imaginative approaches to achieving these goals. I had not been there very long before a little voice began poking me in the subconscious ribs and saying, 'What better way of developing self-confidence and self-discipline than riding? What better way of unlocking emotional cupboards than through a relationship with a horse?'

Somewhat hesitantly, I put forward my ideas to my

superiors and before I knew it, one Friday morning found me heading up the A19 towards Washington with the College minibus and a group of excited students and support workers. Our destination was the Strang Riding Centre for the Disabled. This centre had been purpose-built in the late 1970s with proceeds from the famous 'Blue Peter Clothes Horse Appeal' and had been run on a charitable basis ever since. It was large, modern, superbly run and equipped with an enormous indoor arena that offered safe, comfortable riding throughout the year for disabled children and adults all over the region. Jane Pearson, the manager and instructor, quickly dispelled any nervousness on the part of the Peterlee students, and within a very few weeks 'Equestrian Studies' became a firm favourite on the Bridging timetable.

For myself, it felt too good to be true that as part of my actual job I could work in an environment that I loved so deeply and felt so at home in. As the weeks passed I watched students who had been so nervous on their first ride that they had had to be held on by two helpers, trotting independently around the arena, heads held high, full of confidence. I listened in humble amazement to a student with severe communication difficulties uttering over and over in delight as she patted her horse, 'Good horse, Zephyr! Good horse!' Jane taught the actual riding and I extended the students' knowledge and experience into the stable and into the realm of 'horsecare', so that they could learn to take some responsibility for the horses they were sharing so much that was new with. Of course, as ever, I couldn't achieve everything I wanted. I had students who were wheelchair users who could simply never ride. I knew the answer of course – carriage driving – but the Strang Centre seemed to be entirely devoted to riding.

'Well not exactly entirely,' said Jane mysteriously when I broached the subject with her. 'We were given a small

trap to use with wheelchairs when the centre opened and
we *do* have a pony passed by the RDA for driving.'

I felt an old familiar tingle begin to surge.

'But . . .' I went into fast freeze. 'But, the problems have
been that Beauty – that's the pony – was lame for a very
long time, though she's fine now!' Jane added hastily. 'And
also, she continued, 'we have had no one who is a qualified,
able-bodied whip to teach the driving. Didn't you say
something about being qualified to teach driving?'

Oh yes, I assured her happily, I most certainly was.

'Shall we get the keys for the cart shed? We can drag the
trap out, blow off the cobwebs and you can have a look.'

In the coming weeks I blew the cobwebs off more than
that trap. Beauty, grey, elderly and somewhat astonished,
was backed between the shafts for the first time in ages
and gently reintroduced to her role. A long-lost set of
harness was found, cleaned, reassembled and checked.
Before long our Friday morning minibus contingent
included two students who were wheelchair users; Sharon
who had cerebral palsy and Jason, who suffered from muscular dystrophy. Although plodding slowly around the
arena with Beauty and a disabled student was a far cry
from the thrills of driving Bear, it nevertheless reawakened
my deep personal commitment to Driving for the Disabled.

'Walk on, Beauty!' Sharon would shrill, and away Beauty
would plod and Sharon would glow with the achievement
of exerting her will over something in her world she could
actually control.

I watched the horses and ponies in their busy but unhurried lives at the centre. Most of them were quite elderly,
retired and gifted to the centre by their owners when, for
one reason or another, they could no longer continue with
their normal working lives. Well fed, beautifully cared for,
fussed over by an army of doting trainee grooms. Living
useful, structured, worthwhile lives until they were genu-
inely too old to enjoy work any more. Only suffering or

an inability to work any more, however gently, would
mark the end of these much loved creatures' careers and
then they would be put down, with dignity, and with a
feeling of real loss at the centre. I finally knew what I had
to do, what I was in all conscience honour-bound to do for
Bear.

'He's beautiful,' admitted Jane, looking at the photos I
had offered her. 'Hard to believe he is nearly twenty-one.
Did you say he's a Welsh Cob?'

'Yes, pure bred. I can let you have his papers if you
want.'

'No,' she laughed. 'That's not important here. What is
important is that his temperament is right and that he
settles to working with the clients well; that *he* is happy in
his daily work. Of course, if he is still as active and fit as
you say, he will be used for much more than the disabled
clients.'

'Oh?' I enquired, my heart lifting a little. I was not
entirely sure that Bear would be content to restrict himself
to walking in sedate circles for a year or two yet.

'Certainly. You only see your students in their riding
lessons here. But we also use the centre to train our grooms
for their British Horse Society exams. Some of them get as
high as stage two and we use our younger, fitter horses
for their lessons. So if Bear enjoys dressage and schooling
so much, then he'll get ample opportunity for it. Even a
little low level jumping in the indoor school could be on
the cards. If that's all right with you.' Jane added hastily.

'All right? *All right*? That would be *wonderful* Jane! If
Bear can only be active and busy and, well, needed again
every day, I know he will be happy. It's me that's finding
this so very hard after all these years, you know.'

'Yes, I do understand,' said Jane. 'It's bound to be hard.'

'But I want you to know,' I continued, 'that there simply
isn't anywhere else I would even consider sending him.
It's because I know how well he will be treated and how

much happier he will be doing something worthwhile that I can bring myself to do it at all.'

'Right then.' Ever practical, Jane propelled me out of the office, her shoulder length curls bouncing as she strode purposefully out to the car with me. 'I'll send the wagon on Saturday then?'

'Yes. Thank you. Yes, that will be fine.'

She placed her hand briefly on mine and looking into my somewhat damp eyes, 'Don't worry. He will be fine, and you will see him every week you know! Anytime you want, come to that. Just come and see him.'

'Thank you Jane – for everything.'

With that remembrance, I shook myself back to reality in the corner of the little stable, realizing that the cold was seeping through my bones even sitting on top of my little heap of straw. I had done my crying and was now feeling, if anything, a little ashamed of myself; my tears had been pure selfishness. I realized that the afternoon light was beginning to fade. The owner of the yard and her daughter had gone to a gymkhana some distance away, which had given me the run of the place for the afternoon, for which I was grateful. I finished my mucking out, emptied and washed out Bear's water bucket and tucked the old rug safely in the back of my car. Then I drove slowly down the bumpy cart track to the road, knowing that one of the longest chapters of my life had finally closed.

Because of the assessments and courses at the beginning of the College year, the students did not commence their riding lessons until well into October. I used this as the somewhat feeble excuse to avoid going to Washington. I did phone Jane regularly and received plenty of progress reports, most of them glowing. Bear had settled quickly, happily and completely into the routine of the place, I was assured. He was already a firm favourite with the staff and the clients. Perhaps if I just went to see him it would put my mind at ease? Soon, I promised nervously, I would come soon. He had gone. He had to go. I had to be sure I had accepted this in my heart before I could risk seeing him.

But the unavoidable day finally came and I drove the college minibus up the A19 to Washington with very mixed emotions. A lesson was in progress when we walked in. I suspected Jane had set it up knowing we were arriving that morning. It was a training lesson for the staff and leading the class around the arena was a girl riding Bear. His beautiful silver banner of a tail flowed proudly behind him. Immaculately groomed, his rich, dark red coat glowed with a life of its own as his muscles moved beneath it. As ever, the cadence and rhythm and sheer beauty of watching him work caught my throat and my very breath.

'And walk,' instructed Jane. 'And halt.'

Bear slowed and then stood obediently motionless.

'Good!' said Jane. 'Right, dismount and run up your stirrups. We'll need these horses plus four more for the Peterlee class.'

I watched through blurred eyes while Bear's rider covered his neck with an ecstasy of kisses and pats and then produced a tube of Polo mints, which he gobbled with gusto.

'Hello Carol,' smiled Jane. 'Well, here he is. Looking well don't you think? And working well too.'

I smiled back at Jane and nodded, though actual words would not come. I moved slowly towards Bear with an extended hand. 'Hello, bonny lad,' I said softly.

He stopped in mid-munch as if puzzled and then, having sniffed my hand, resumed his munching, totally unconcerned.

'Are you Bear's mum?' asked the girl rider, who had reappeared from running up his stirrup on the off side.

'Yes,' I laughed. 'I suppose I am!'

'Well,' she said, almost reverently, 'I think he is smashing! I didn't like jumping at all till I started with Bear; but he always goes over, makes me feel safe somehow. I can't believe I can ride such a famous horse! Jane has told us all about what he has done you know. I am glad you have come to see him. I think he is very happy here – you can tell.' She blethered on softly and happily, fussing over Bear all the while, obviously sincere in her admiration. And yes, I could tell he was happy; different again from the animal that had gazed at me with puzzled, mournful eyes from the corner of the little field where he had been living out most of his life a few weeks before.

The lesson for my students got underway. With astonishing gentleness Bear walked around the arena with one of my very nervous students on his back and me by his side.

'This is Bear,' I told him, 'he's very special and don't worry, he'll look after you! That's it: just hold the reins and pull very gently. Say "Whoa, Bear" and he'll stop for you. You try.'

'Whoa Bear!' he said with great disbelief, but Bear nevertheless obediently stopped.

'That's it! Pat him and tell him he is a good boy. Well done. Now, a gentle squeeze with your legs and ask him to "Walk on". Come on, you're riding this horse. You're in charge.'

'Walk on, Bear!' the boy said, the confidence already growing in his voice. Bear's swift response to the command resulted in a huge grin and a spontaneous 'Good boy!'

Conwy Blaze, beloved to so many as 'Bear', had just taken another human soul the first few tentative steps along the path to discovery, achievement and sharing. I think I loved him more in that moment than down all the years I had been privileged to share with him.

'Come on,' I said to the student at the end of the ride. 'I'll show you how to put him away properly.'

We took Bear to his stable and the student watched

carefully as I took Bear's saddle and bridle off and fastened on his rugs. Bear succumbed to my fussing tolerantly, as he had done so many hundreds of times. The thread of riding and driving that had run through my life for so long, and which I had thought lost, appeared to be going to weave itself into a new and very different pattern. There wasn't a trap at the Strang Centre big enough for Bear to use for Disabled Driving, but what if, what if . . .

So many years ago, Great-aunt Meg had left her money to me as a legacy 'in trust'. That trust had been placed by me in the talents of this remarkable horse. Now, in the evening of his life, he had the opportunity to use these talents in a unique and quite wonderful way.

'Goodbye, bonny lad,' I whispered, running my hand down his smooth, muscled neck one last time before leaving him in peace.

Conwy Blaze: my pride, my joy, my friend. The legacy was now his to pass on.